Mediation of Environmental Disputes
A Sourcebook

Mediation of Environmental Disputes

A Sourcebook

Scott Mernitz

with a foreword by John Busterud

PRAEGER SPECIAL STUDIES • PRAEGER SCIENTIFIC

Published in 1980 by Praeger Publishers
CBS Educational and Professional Publishing
A Division of CBS, Inc.
521 Fifth Avenue, New York, New York 10017 U.S.A.

©1980 by Scott Mernitz

Cataloging in Publication Number 80-7503

ISBN 0-03-055281-8

0123456789 056 987654321

Printed in the United States of America

Contents

LIST OF FIGURES

ACKNOWLEDGMENTS

The original manuscript for this book was a Ph.D. thesis in the interdisciplinary Land Resources Degree Program, Institute for Environmental Studies, University of Wisconsin, Madison. I am indebted to this program for providing the educational framework for my course of study.

Many people contributed their time and thoughts to this work. To all, both named and unnamed, I express my thanks for their help and encouragement. I especially thank my advisor and chairman, George Dury, for his counsel on the practical and substantive aspects of the thesis preparation. The other advisors and members of my committee deserve thanks as well: Francis Hole, Carlisle Runge, John Steinhart, Henry Hart, and Eugene Wilkening. All contributed comments from their disciplinary perspectives which helped me to balance the interdisciplinary analysis. Any remaining errors, however, are solely mine.

I dedicate this work to my wife, Sue; the task would have been doubly difficult without her. I must also mention my father, Richard J. Mernitz, who originally proposed the notion of environmental mediation to me about 1970. This work carries out one of his many innovative ideas.

I am also grateful to the staff at RESOLVE, notably John Busterud and Barbara Vaughn, for their editorial suggestions.

FOREWORD

In the spring of 1978, RESOLVE published "Environmental Mediation: An Effective Alternative?" This was a report on a three-day conference held at Reston, Virginia in January of that year. Co-sponsored by the Aspen Institute for Humanistic Studies and the Sierra Club, the conference brought together more than 50 participants to consider the status of environmental mediation and the prospects for its wider application. Our report not only summarized the conference proceedings but included a series of brief case histories of disputes which had been successfully resolved by means of mediation or other alternatives to litigation.

Mediation of Environmental Disputes represents a much more comprehensive study of the same subject. Dr. Mernitz begins by taking a broad look at the nature and history of environmental conflict in this country, then focuses on the role mediation can play in helping settle these disputes. There is much in this book which will be of practical value. For example, Dr. Mernitz describes a variety of tools which can be used by a prospective mediator to analyze environmental disputes.

Another virtue of this book is the variety of perspectives—economic, legal, political, and psychological—which Dr. Mernitz has brought to bear on his subject. As this book demonstrates, environmental conflicts are often complex and multi-dimensional. The more resources a mediator has at his or her disposal, the greater the likelihood of ultimate success.

Mediation represents but one of many techniques available for settling environmental disputes. RESOLVE is working actively to promote all promising approaches. However, mediation remains a particularly important technique, and we hope that publication of this book will contribute to its more effective use.

John Busterud
President,
RESOLVE
Center for Environmental
Conflict Resolution

INTRODUCTION

This is a book about the resolution of environmental conflicts. Mediation, a technique long used to resolve labor disputes and, more recently, to settle community disputes, is assessed as a means of resolving conflicts concerning the use and development of natural resources.

This book examines disputes from various disciplinary perspectives and arrives at a set of questions that can help a mediator assess a given conflict. Dr. Mernitz offers conclusions about the mediability of environmental disputes and the viability of mediation as a conflict resolution tool.

Mediation of Environmental Disputes can serve as a handbook for the prospective mediator. By consulting the appropriate sections, the prospective mediator may augment his or her knowledge of the dimensions of environmental conflict, the various actors and influences in environmental disputes, certain existing records he or she might use to aid a mediation effort, the nature of the mediation function in social and psychological terms, existing environmental mediation efforts, negotiated agreements, and conflict case studies.

Disputes over resource use will be with us for many years to come. The approach suggested in this book could well minimize the expensive and frustrating delays that have so often accompanied natural resource decisionmaking.

I.
The Scope of
Environmental Conflict

"Preservation versus development," "protectionists versus recreationists," and "environment versus economy" are phrases which characterize environmental conflict. Disputes over the use of resources are not, however, a simple dichotomy of forces. Environmental conflict, ever increasing in the United States, is a complex, changing interplay of diverse interests and goals.

Mediation, a technique familiar to persons working with labor/management and community conflicts, can be used for resolving these multi-interest environmental disputes. Its application has resulted in win-win outcomes for all parties concerned, often with a minimum of time and expense. This can occur because the mediator is the balancer; he is the catalyst for achieving a solution, compromise, or common, middle position among conflicting positions. The goal of environmental mediation is to promote a balance among diverse interests.

But, as with all promising new ideas, there is the danger that mediation may be inappropriately used, fail to provide the hoped-for results, and be discarded. On the other hand, it may be under-used because it is not yet institutionalized. To help avoid these possibilities, we need 1) an objective evaluation of mediation as a technique for settlement of environmental disputes, as illustrated by analysis of several existing disputes and their amenability to mediation during various stages of conflict; and 2) development of techniques for evaluation of environmental disputes which will allow the prospective mediator to understand the issues and to better mediate the dispute if requested to do so. These are the objectives of this book.

Environmental conflict can be examined in various conceptual and intellectual ways. The following discussion will illustrate the diverse nature of environmental conflict, out of which implications for mediation of environmental disputes can be made.

ATTITUDES AND POLITICAL CULTURE

Popular attitudes and important trends in intellectual thought can increase our understanding of the diversity of opinion regarding environmental conflict. Figure 1, as discussed in the following paragraphs, attempts to designate some of the parallel, yet convergent streams of thought which have shaped our present attitudes toward the environment.

The historic roots of our ecologic crisis have been discussed in excellent fashion by White (1967). He refers especially to the Judeo-Christian dogmas as having major impact. In the Book of Genesis (1:28), man is encouraged by God to replenish the earth, and to subdue it, and to have dominion over all living things. The main thrust of Biblical teaching is to inspire dominance of nature by man (for a detailed discussion of man's changing ideas of nature through history, see Glacken, 1956).

We have, in the late 1970s, a composite view of man and environment, influenced by many ideas. Organized efforts toward pollution control by government were spurred by Earth Day, 1970, a preservationist, "ecological conscience" celebration which had great initial impact. Partial rejection of the "more is better" philosophy of exponential growth followed. Respect for business enterprise remains, tempered by a concern for diminishing natural resources. Environment, as seen by different religions, cultures, and influential thinkers, takes on special meaning when conflict over resource use or development confronts us and our personal philosophies.

If one theme emerges from this discussion, it is the theme of man's concern for himself. From the man-centered Biblical view, to Marsh's personification of nature, to Pinchot's concern for the common good, man has placed himself first.

The placement is not a clear, finely drawn one, however. Figure 1 is shown as a moving stream of ideas, but with no attempt to indicate by arrows the influence of theories on successive views. Mixing, formation, and reformation have in fact occurred. It is thus understandably difficult to describe a single predominant view of environmental conflict today.

It is possible to make one statement: public attitudes and opinions regarding environmental conflicts are diverse. The diversity of opinion, changing with each issue and situation, suggest that our political culture is diverse and implies that, for a majority, a common, balanced view of each environmental conflict might be attained. Most of us, individually, are neither preservationists nor developers; we are somewhere in between.

TECHNOLOGY

Technology often causes environmental conflict. If only machines did not take such huge chunks out of the earth; if only so much waste were not discharged into the waterway; if only so many pollutants were not emitted in such magnitude by so many automobiles—such are common complaints of those concerned with the environment. Environmental degradation consequently becomes a question of degree of change. Man can cope and has coped with natural changes for many centuries; it is the whirling mass of changes produced by technology that causes major problems (Ogburn, 1957: 8).

Technologists agree that the machines themselves are not the cause of environmental degradation. Man produces the machines and determines their use. Fred Knelman (1971: 48), in an introduction to a section entitled "Technology and the Environmental Crisis" in *1984 and All That,* states "pollution is a direct consequence of the anti-ecological nature of a laissez-faire technology not properly assessed and controlled, and designed only to reinforce existing political and economic structures." Man, after all, does the assessing and controlling and designing. Lewis Mumford (1970: 413) believes that a profound alteration of our personal desires, habits and ideals is necessary to avert the environmental degradation hastened by the use of inappropriate technology. Dennis Gabor (1970: 76) agrees that science and technology are mismatched with the institutional structure of our society and with the basic nature of man.

The solution to these problems of technology returns to men and their diversity of opinion regarding environmental conflict. Two-thirds of a voting public may oppose construction of a power plant employing a new technology, but two-thirds of that same group may favor a plant of any type in face of power shortages. Man's control over technology is as varied as his needs, wants, values, and priorities.

George F. Marsh, often called the father of conservation, espoused his views of man's responsibility for nature in the 1860s. His book *Man and Nature* (1864) encouraged conservation, restoration, and man's relationship to living and non-living things. Marsh's close feeling for the equality of man and nature led him to speak fondly, for example, of "the personality (of) a respectable oak" (quoted in the introduction by David Lowenthal, ed.)

Environmental thought in the early 1900s was influenced by geographers Ellen Churchill Semple, (e.g., see Semple, 1901, "The Anglo-Saxons of the Kentucky Mountains") and Ellsworth Huntington (see *Civilization and Climate,* 1924), who proposed "environmentalism" as a theory of nature's dominance of man's existence and well-being. The theory is more correctly termed "environmental determinism" as it pertains to today's view of environmentalists.

At about the same time (1893), Frederick Jackson Turner's thesis of the American Frontier and its role in shaping American expansion, invention, development, and growth became popularized (Mikesell, 1960). Turner's thesis and Horace Greeley's famous advice to "Go West, young man" influenced many immigrants to the east coast U.S. in the early 1900s.

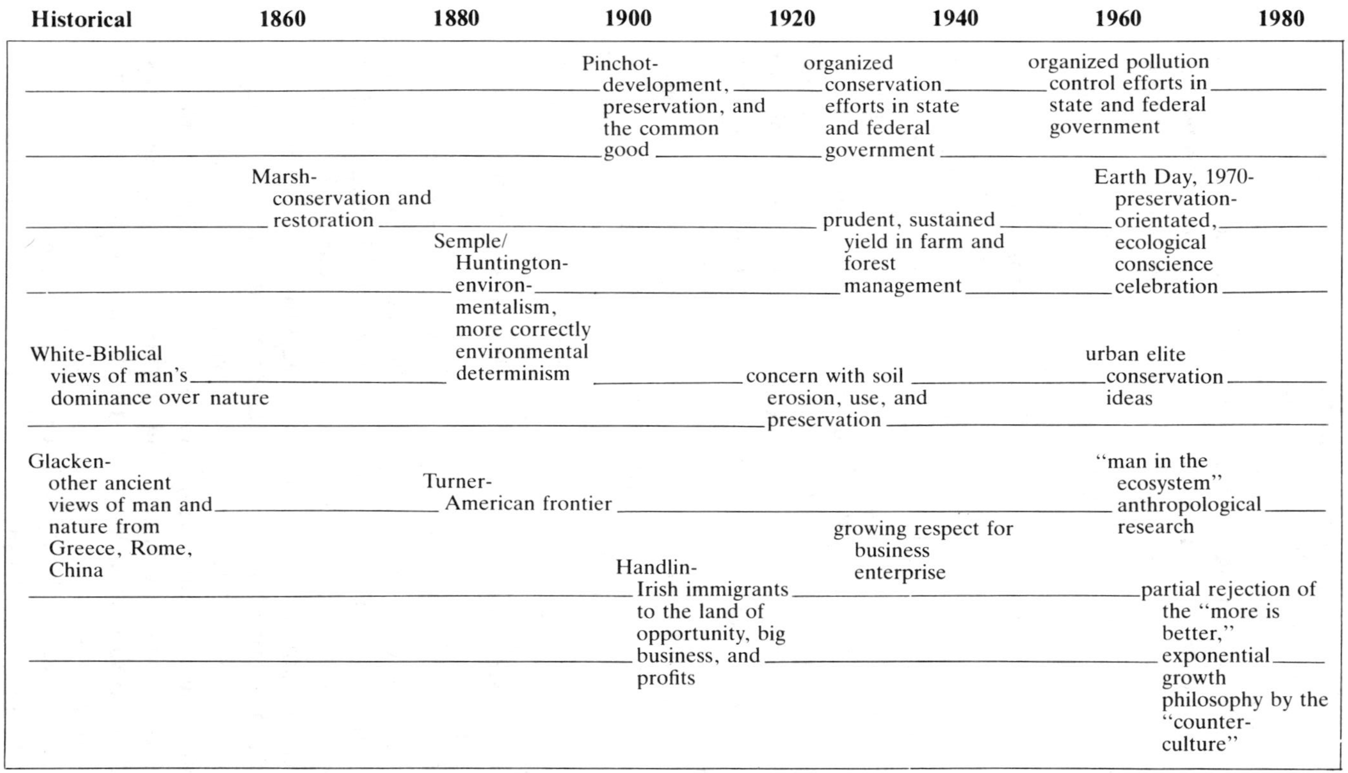

Fig. 1.   Representative influences on present environmental thinking. Displayed from left to right is a moving and intermingling stream of ideas and trends.

America was characterized (in the immigrant's minds) as a land of opportunity, big business, and profits (Handlin, 1959). This stream of influence emerges in our respect for business enterprise, which was nurtured through the first half of the twentieth century. This respect has been tempered, however, by the outright condemnation of business enterprise in recent years by the "counter-culture."

Gifford Pinchot, Chief Forester in the Theodore Roosevelt Administration in the early 1900s, did much to influence current conservation thinking. Pinchot's principles of natural resource use, encouraging "development, preservation, (and) the common good" (Pinchot, 1910: 49), led to the practice of prudent, sustained yield in farming and forestry management. The magnitude of soil erosion in the 1930s legitimized Pinchot's principles and aided the establishment of organized conservation agencies in state and federal governments. Today we have organized state and federal agencies not only for conservation but also for its more applied form: pollution control.

An urban elite conservation movement paralleled government conservation efforts in the mid-1900s. Concerned citizens, mostly in the upper income classes, urged the general public to become informed and enthusiastic about the environment through organizations such as the Audubon Society, the Izaak Walton League, and later, outspoken groups such as the Sierra Club.

Numerous anthropological studies have contributed to our current ideas of environment and man. For example, the study by Spindler and Spindler of Menomini Indian acculturization (1971) and William Laughlin's article on the Aleuts and their island existence (1975) suggest that these tribes were, before Western influence, well integrated into their ecosystems. The combined attributes of conservation, preservation, and resource use within carrying capacity took place within the context of pagan animism. These people were neither preservationists nor developers, but functioned as an integral part of their ecosystem.

The technological fix is often used to mollify environmental conflict or to postpone threats from the natural environment (e.g. floods), because technology is easy to apply (Heberlein, 1974). Technology is applied to reduce variability in the physical environment. However, direct application of technology ignores two other ways of dealing with environmental conflict. Heberlein terms these other ways the cognitive and the structural fixes. The cognitive fix views man as a rational, flexible actor in his environment who will modify his behavior if persuaded to do so. New knowledge encourages new actions. The structural fix modifies human behavior by modifying the physical setting or structure in which the action takes place. When employed, physical structure promotes a change in action or development.

Use of cognitive and structural fixes in the environmental conflict situation, especially that of cognitive fix, means input from the parties to the dispute. The diversity of opinion and new information is best integrated to solve the problem by a third party, a mediator. It may be, too, that structural fixes for solution can best be considered and approved, or rejected, with the help of a third party. Often technological fix is also part of the settlement. The mediator, however, may facilitate "human solutions" to the conflict; solutions which Hardin (1968) urges for consideration in his classic "Tragedy of the Commons."

The place of knowledge, information, and technology in environmental conflict can be examined in yet another way. Conflicts about environment and growth are increasingly created by forward thrusts in science. These thrusts create an awareness of possible serious and irreparable damage, and an uncertainty that the technology being applied is correct for mankind's long-term benefit. Science is, after all, an art, subject to the fallibilities of all arts practiced by humans (Caldwell, 1970: 147).

The mediation of scientific uncertainties as they apply to particular environmental conflicts will involve a consensus of interpretation. The courts have been continually baffled by adversary proceedings in which scientific experts from one side refute claims of experts from the other side. Recent proposals for a science court, although containing problems, exemplify this notion and accent the need for a different forum for scientific evidence (*Science,* 1976: 129; Environmental Science & Technology, 1976). Mediation/negotiation sessions would, in theory, accommodate scientific evidence and would serve as an effective forum in which scientific and technical issues may be resolved.

LAW

The legal view of environmental conflict is distilled from the language of case law, environmental legislation, and legal opinion. Environmental case law of the early 1970s provides much procedural definition and some important substantive interpretations of laws regarding environmental policy, clean water, clean air, and related matters. Aside from confusing legalities, the essence of the legal view of environmental conflict concerns a balancing of interests. Judge Miles Lord, in *U.S. v. Reserve Mining* (1947b) notes "any environmental litigation must involve a balancing of economic dislocation with any environmental benefits." He goes on to state "the Court cannot honor profit over human life." In an earlier opinion, Justice William Douglas's dissent in *Sierra Club v. Morton* (1972) follows a similar theme in the argument for legal standing (and animate characteristics, in a sense) for inanimate objects. Douglas urges that the environment be given the same legal standing as humans, in order that spokesmen for each position are of equal stature.

Concern for human life and for the life-sustaining environment are evident in the language of environmental legislation. The National Environmental Policy Act (1969), Clean Air Act Amendments (1970), and Federal Water Pollution Control Act Amendments (1972) respectively state, in their introductory sections, that each appropriate Federal agency shall

> identify and develop methods or procedures...which will insure that presently unquantified environmental amenities and values may be given appropriate consideration in decisionmaking along with economic and technical considerations (Sec. 102 (B));

or that the purpose of the law is

> to protect and enhance the quality of the Nation's air resources so as to promote the public health and welfare and the productive capacity of its population (Sec. 101 (b)(1));

or that the law's objective is

> to restore and maintain the chemical, physical, and biological integrity of the Nation's waters (Sec. 101 (a)).

The language of the three passages is similar, in that human use of natural resources is desired, coupled with elevation of resources to human status by speaking of their integrity and amenity. Interpretations of, and challenges to, the legal, human traits granted to the environment have resulted in considerable environmental litigation.

The way law regards environmental conflict may be summarized as follows: (1) the law shows a concern for the quality of human life over economic benefits; (2) the law has considered, and frequently attempts to promote, inanimate objects as living for legal purposes; and (3) the law looks for a middle ground, or balance, between environmental (life-sustaining) values and economic profit. Since legal procedure often has difficulty in handling environmental conflict, given the three statements, need for another conflict management procedure has arisen. Environmental mediation is such a procedure.

POLITICAL INTERESTS

Any environment-versus-growth conflict involves diverse political interests. Popular ideas and their influence on present political culture, as discussed under the first heading in this chapter, are only a portion of the total political force which influences an environment-versus-growth decision. An example from a current controversy will illustrate this point.

Many communities throughout the United States are considering legal procedures to limit their growth (see Sager, 1976). The opposition includes civil liberties groups, who protest even traditional zoning practices as exclusionary, the housing industry (including construction trades, home furnishings manufacturers and related interests), utilities, and virtually every service industry that could ever hope to locate in a particular community.

Proponents of growth limits in urbanized areas wish to perpetuate the status quo. They like their neighborhoods and the convenience of nearby service functions. They dislike the prospect of more pollution of air and water, more congestion and noise, and destruction of the pleasant character of their environment.

Both sides recognize that land use controls and land use decisions will have an immediate and drastic impact on their quality of life. Their difference is over conflicts of values; a difference which creates genuine discord.

The decision to limit or not to limit growth is a political one. Each field of force in the conflict is composed of diverse interests, with specific clienteles, lobbyists, funding and working arrangements. Such diverse interests, which imply polarization of values, would seem to constrain mediation efforts. The mediator, however, looks for the common areas, the areas of agreement rather than of disagreement between opposing forces. In the example of urban growth limits, he may see that a healthful environment and planned growth are desired by both sides, and may be able to facilitate a settlement which provides for these factors and also for a fair share of housing and services for underprivileged groups.

To solve these problems, Sager suggests that a combination of arrangements, to include affirmation of some zoning, partial diminution of local autonomy, and accommodation by every community of its fair share of regional housing needs, will likely come to pass in many communities. The political decision can emerge from several forums: referenda, courts, legislatures, or less formal meetings. In sum, each line of policy and field of force presents its partly unique opportunities and constraints to the mediator, as also to traditional intervenors in environmental conflict.

ECONOMICS

The economic view of environmental conflict is based on a familiar theme: public welfare. Whether discussing equity, internalizing external costs, optimal level of pollution, pareto admissibility, or non-zero-sum decisions, the concern is for man's well-being.

According to economists, environmental conflict is fundamentally an economic problem. Greater use of material goods produces a deterioration in environmental conditions because of increased extraction, processing, use, and waste (Downs, 1973). Deterioration of environmental conditions due to economic prosperity and increased use of material goods produces concern for environmental quality.

Environmental conflict involves questions of cost. Each natural resource exploitation activity has internal costs, for which the collective good (or intended product) is produced, and external costs, which cause environmental damage. The latter, a spillover effect, suggests that an internalization of external costs may solve environmental conflicts. Unfortunately, because property rights, demarcation, and transferability do not exist for air, water, and land resources of individuals, precise internalization is not feasible (Mishan, 1973: 93-94). Economic compensation may, however, aid some settlements.

Others discuss human well-being as influenced by human activity. Ruff (1973: 41-42) states that the "divergence between private and social costs is the fundamental cause of pollution of all types." The emphasis is on social costs and social conditions. He states further that economics may suggest ways for achieving the many possible efficient states of public welfare, but that the political process must choose which state will prevail. Economics and politics are joined in a decision that is *pareto admissible* — i.e., no other decision exists that is just as satisfactory (confers equal benefits) to all parties and more satisfactory to some of them (see Dorfman and Jacoby, 1971: 184).[1]

For purposes of this introduction, a final way in which economics depicts environmental conflict is derived from game theory. If most dispute settlements are viewed as non-zero-

---

[1]One caveat is appropriate: discussions of pareto optimization (and a win-win situation, see following paragraph) imply, theoretically, that nobody loses. In consideration of long-term goals and maximum societal benefits, such might be the case. In the immediate, real-life situation, however, everybody loses something tangible when compromise occurs.

sum games (defined as settlements in which each side gains benefits), implications for mediation are present. A non-zero-sum settlement satisfies some desires of each party and promotes a friendly, problem-solving relationship (see Hall, 1973). The mediator can develop such a relationship by adopting a conflict management strategy which emphasizes the win-win philosophy.

Discussion in this chapter has emphasized two basic characteristics of environmental conflict: (1) the subject is interdisciplinary in nature; and (2) as characterized by various disciplines, environmental conflict has several qualities which suggest mediation as a feasible settlement technique. These basic statements will be explored in the following chapters.

II.
Further Discussion of Environmental Disputes

THE ACTORS

The actors emerging on the U.S. environmental scene in 1970 were a diverse mixture. Age differences were apparent in some value conflicts. Those who experienced the Great Depression of the 1930s tended to support the traditional values of hard work, prosperity, and use of the environment for man's greatest benefit. The younger generation, having experienced no economic hard times on a large scale, often characterized the older generation as despoilers and opportunists who caused irreparable damage to the environment for the purpose of private gain. The dichotomy was of a general nature only. Age, like political interests or personal attitudes, is not an absolute determinant of environmental orientation.

A sampling of the actors of 1970 by occupation is more relevant than other factors for a discussion of environmental mediation. No matter what the personal inclination, occupation determines income, and personal well-being is a major determinant of how one perceives environmental conflict. Money talks: in the American West, some even say it has the power to make water run uphill.

Politicians make the laws that regulate use of the environment. Elected officials were quick to grasp the significance and impact of public environmental concern in 1970. The politician is oriented toward remedies to social problems—laws that will prohibit environmental despoilation by regulating development, establishing pollutant emission standards, and providing public money for treating effluents (Nelson, 1970). Although many attempted to attach their names to "environmental concern" in the public mind, among the most effective legislators were Senators Muskie, Jackson, and Nelson, all of whom had records in environmental legislation that began well before 1970.

Administrators who carried out the legislative mandates have lacked the notoriety of political figures. Indeed, the most effective administrators have stayed out of politics by necessity. Their public remarks and educational materials have tended to be objective statements of what is to be done (according to legislative policy) and what has been done thus far. In environmental conflict, good administrators straddle the fence, attempting to balance between conflicting and often irreconcilable demands. Consistent policy earns respect, however.

The business community has been inconvenienced by environmental legislation and its requirements. A portion of that community has benefitted from the demand for pollution control equipment and environmental consulting services, but most corporations continually bemoan the increased costs of regulations and controls, the effects on profits, and the time (often in excess of established deadlines) that is needed for full compliance. The bottom line is increased costs for the consumer.

One might cynically state that business is buying time and will eventually take the lead in the environmental movement in order to control it (Ridgeway, 1970: 16-17). Whatever the case, profits will govern most, if not all, corporate decisions in environmental conflict situations. Some companies have a commendable record of public service projects; unfortunately these companies are in the minority.

Educators, scientists, researchers, and others from assorted academic disciplines have been commentators on the environmental scene. Collectively, they identified the values, such as our beliefs in economic efficiency and specialization, which tended to cause environmental problems (Wager, 1970). They also identified social and political factors, such as human population growth and institutional and legislative misman- agement, that contributed to the problems (Budowski, 1973: 19).

Perhaps the most durable contribution of the scientific community came from the ecologists. While public concern grew, ecologists took a leading role as those studying the vital issue of man's impact on natural systems. Ecologic studies ranged from the sophisticated, quantified, and technical bio- mass analyses of Eugene Odum to the more popular and accessible works of Barry Commoner on science and the public welfare. Ecologists and their colleagues in the scientific com- munity contributed by attempting to define pollution and by classifying environmental disturbances, impacts, and prob- lems. Their work formed the intellectual basis for much of our environmental outlook. Of no less impact are the legislative and administrative remedies based on this primary research.

In addition to the specialized contributions of ecologists, a larger, more diverse group of environmentalists were and are an important force in our society. Environmentalists vary from strict protectionists to lobbyists to hikers to legal experts to citizens picking up trash along river banks. Many are ori- ented toward preservation; others temper their concern with a realization of the necessities of our civilization. If a developer may be labeled a proponent of change, an environmentalist group is often identified as opposing such change.

The individual consumer, mentioned briefly in a preceding paragraph, deserves further discussion. Each of us, through consumer action, influences the political, business, and though less than the others, the intellectual community. Consumer action can influence the move to smaller cars, the phase out of fluorocarbons in aerosol cans, or the projected need for coal- fired power plants. Collectively, consumers are the most pow- erful group of all.

ASSESSING DISPUTANTS' POSITIONS

How does the mediator assess each of the identified groups in an environmental dispute? How does he rank the

relevant factors? The following *suggested* ranking reflects those
factors which shape a party's position on a given dispute:
   (in order of importance)
   (1) quality of life, especially as affected by income source;
   (2) political issues;
   (3) other values;
   (4) ecological quality.

In evaluating these factors, one must recognize that they
are interactive, that the parties have multiple objectives, and
thus the ranking may not hold true in all cases. The ranking
will be explored in later discussion and analysis.

To illustrate the ranking, a land use conflict involving construction of a coal-fired power plant on the eastern Great
Plains of Colorado might be used. The prospective mediator
should first be concerned with the income sources of each of
the conflict participants, individually or collectively. It is my
judgment that income source is a strong indicator of a favorable or unfavorable view of plant construction.

Second, the mediator might assess feelings pro or con
with reference to the relevant political issues. Preservation of
agricultural land and water may influence income, but it also
may determine the future of a state region. Power plant construction could damage the potential for irrigated agriculture,
remove parcels of land from agricultural production incremen-
tally, and change the economic base of an area. Decisions by
elected officials regarding such situations are expressions of the
political process, and the desire for political clout is definitely
an expression of self-interest.

Third, certain parties often come into conflict because of
their value judgments about plant construction. Growth policies, conservationist or preservationist feelings, control of
technology and other value conflicts might arise which must be
handled. The mediator should recognize the importance of
such values because of their potential for causing impasse. He
should also recall that income source and political ambitions
often shape one's values and thus be prepared for the major
influence self-interest will have on shaping negotiations.

Fourth, (unfortunately, from a natural sciences perspective) are those factors involving actual impacts of development

on ecological quality. The ecologists made many aware of the need for balanced and diverse ecosystems in land, air, and water, but our collective society expresses only minor concern for such factors when preceded by income source, political issues, and values.

The ecosystems factor clearly overlaps with the values category, just as there is overlap among self-interest, political issues, and values. Effective intervention in environmental conflict therefore requires interdisciplinary analysis.

OTHER INFLUENCES ON DISPUTE PERCEPTION

The four highly relevant factors, discussed above, do not address all of the important influences on dispute perception. Other factors determine how a person approaches conflict and behaves while involved in it.

Several of these factors or influences on perception of environmental conflict can be loosely grouped under environmental education. Included here are media coverage, public information and education by various means, scientific and technical information, and the impact of environmental litigation. A brief discussion of these influences will clarify the setting for third party intervention.

MEDIA

The media inform most of us of recent developments in efforts to curtail pollution of air, water, and land. We also learn, through television, radio, newspapers, and magazines, of land use conflicts over such issues as power plant siting, recreational developments, and extractive mining. It follows that when a dispute is initiated which affects one's personal well-being, the information provided by the media is central to one's perception of the dispute. A study by Beane and Ross (1974), for example, indicates that a majority of citizens are well-informed on the economic consequences of nuclear power plant development, but lack knowledge of the environmental impacts. Such statements speak to the effective media efforts of public utilities and to the priority list of relevant factors offered earlier in this chapter.

Persons familiar with land use conflicts suggest, not surprisingly, that effective control of the media is essential to conflict resolution. The intervenor must minimize the natural tendency of newsmen to look for conflict, because conflict makes news. Practitioners of environmental mediation disagree somewhat on use of the media, however. Most agree that if the negotiations are at a delicate stage, an inflammatory news story can hamper progress (e.g., see Cormick and Patton, 1977: 4). Conversely, properly timed news stories supporting the mediation effort, encouraging reasonableness, and promoting the benefits of settlement for all concerned can generate public support and aid conciliation (Fradin, 1976).

Most of the information we are aware of is public—that is, it is meant for public consumption and understanding. Beyond lies the shadowy realm of scientific and technical information. Such information is digested for and fed to the public by the science and technical writers employed by the media. But digestion is often interpretation, and interpretation is often opinion.

It appears that when the largest mass of experts receiving the most publicity discourage the use of aerosol cans a slow trend in consumer behavior follows. The media are responsible. Legislation and administrative action may follow shortly. By itself, one piece of scientific research is confusing to the average citizen. The confusion is heightened by conflicting testimony of experts on that issue. Scientific and technical information has impact on dispute perception only if it is simplified, repeated, and reinforced by other studies or opinions.

LEGISLATION

Environmental legislation, exemplified by federal and state laws regarding air pollution, water pollution, solid waste, and environmental policy, is playing a significant role in environmental dispute perception. By now almost everyone has heard of environmental impact statements. Most persons know industry cannot pollute wantonly. The media are also making us aware of industry payments, primarily to states, for past violations of pollution control laws and for clean-up and research and development programs to mitigate the problems.

Litigation concerning federal and state environmental statutes is beyond the grasp of the average citizen. Only when case law concerns a major development influencing our future lifestyle (like the Alaska oil pipeline) does environmental litigation come to public attention. Landmark suits contesting provisions of the National Environmental Policy Act (NEPA) and the air and water pollution acts have certainly had both direct and indirect influences on the siting, construction and operation of many developments. But laws and their interpretations, like scientific and technical information, attract little public interest unless they are popularized for some reason.

VALUES

Human values, a relevant factor in environmental disputes, deserve further analysis. Numerous studies in sociology and social psychology have analyzed conflict among individuals and groups in experimental and real-life situations. Suffice it to say, for purposes of this overview, that human behavior and values are of central importance to the magnitude and intensity of conflict. More detailed discussion on this topic will follow in a later chapter.

INCIDENCE AND PROBABILITY OF FUTURE ENVIRONMENTAL CONFLICT

We have spoken of the actors on the environmental scene and of the influences on perceptions of environmental conflict by various parties. Since actors, perceptions, and circumstances are components of environmental disputes, it follows that their prominence would give an indirect prognosis for the future incidence and probability of such disputes. But are there direct indicators? If so, what can one conclude about the projected trends, and hence about the need for persons to work in settlement of environmental conflicts?

The environmental literature of the early 1970s included some predictions about the future of environmental concern. It was natural that the initial indignation over despoliation of the environment would be followed by explanations, analyses, and assessments of the strength and durability of what seemed to be a major American social enterprise. Americans were also concerned about how the rest of the world perceived this movement and was influenced by it. Alden Doud (1972), for example, had no doubt early in the decade that U.S. interest in environmental questions would survive the 70s. Doud maintained this belief in spite of the foreign characterization of Americans as getting involved in this or that only to lose interest a short time later.

Doud was apparently right. Some seven or eight years later there are direct indications that the environmental movement is here to stay. The annual Environmental Quality Index as compiled by the National Wildlife Federation expresses disappointment with the lack of improvement in several areas during 1975, but notes *National Wildlife,* 1976: 29) that polls still (in January, 1976) show undiminished public support for environmental objectives. A random sampling of 3500 students in 20 colleges and universities during the spring of 1976 shows environment as the issue that concerned this group most, ahead of inflation, unemployment, quality of education, poverty, women's rights, and other issues *Playboy,* 1976: 169).

A recent poll (Carter, 1979) confirms that the American public continues to support environmental protection, with over one-half of those surveyed favoring a strongly worded statement advocating high standards and requirements, and the need for continuing improvement regardless of costs. The poll's results gain added weight when one considers its timing: shortly after the passage of the anti-inflation, anti-big government Proposition 13 in California, in the midst of rising concern over environmental regulation fueling this inflation, and following a U.S. Supreme Court decision stopping the Tellico Dam in Tennessee in order to protect an endangered fish species, the snail darter.

Bill Gilbert (1976), in an excellent review article, states that "environmentalism has occupied more of us, cost us more, made more work for us than any other social reform movement of our time." While this statement should be qualified in consideration of such social reform movements as civil rights and the welfare system, the remark and its documentation do illustrate the significance of the environmental movement.

Gilbert does support his statement with solid evidence. He cites the billions of dollars that federal, state, and local governments and private industry have spent on pollution control, the thousands of persons who work in public and private environmental industries, and the scores of private organizations with specific environmental programs, whose total members number in the millions. Environmental laws and regulations significantly affect the daily life of each of us. More than 7,000 federal EISs (environmental impact statements) have been filed since 1970.

The CEQ (Council on Environmental Quality), in support of Gilbert's premise, notes that the number of EISs has increased every year except 1975. An increase was expected in 1976, however, due to expansion of the scope of the EIS process to the Federal Energy Administration (now U.S. Department of Energy) and Consumer Product Safety Commission (CEQ, 1976: 346).

The CEQ has other illustrative data and discussions in the "Conditions and Trends" section of its 1976 report (CEQ, 1976: 187-198). "Energy production and use are perhaps the most important determinants of environmental quality," the report states. Each of us knows or has known of a recent controversy over the siting of an energy facility. Our present national energy policy, relying on "hard" energy technology and ever-diminishing, ever-costly resources, will almost certainly generate many new environmental disputes in the years to come. Even if our course changes to "soft" energy sources—wind, solar, biological waste conversion, and geothermal energy in small, local plants rather than large, regional ones—the transition period will likely include much conflict regarding energy production and use. And energy policy disputes will be supplemented by other conflicts involving various air, water, and land pollutants since, as CEQ notes, few of these pollutants are expected to decrease in occurrence by the year 2000. Groups will be at odds over health effects, not to mention the other social, ecologic, and economic consequences of greater pollutant loading.

The social consequences are and will be staggering. For example, Gilbert notes that since 1973, when the U.S. judicial system began classifying environmental actions, the number of such actions has increased annually from 270 (1973) through 343 (1974) to 406 (1975).

The states recognize the trend, although specific data are difficult to assemble. Nonetheless, informal discussions with personnel of the Wisconsin Department of Natural Resources and Colorado Land Use Commission (in two dissimilar states with dissimilar regulatory problems) reinforce the notion that environmental conflict is increasing. More regulations mean more complaints; more complaints mean two or more parties (often private individuals and government) in conflicting roles.

A trend in key word usage is evolving in environmental disputes. Statements by those on various sides of the environmental questions show expanded use of the words "trade-offs," "negotiation," and "compromise." Grant Thompson of the Environmental Law Institute, as quoted in Gilbert's article, notes "increasingly we are becoming members and consultants to policy-making and regulatory groups. Our input tends to make decisions more acceptable to environmentalists and thus tends to avoid legal confrontation."

In sum, it is likely that the incidence and probability of environmental disputes will increase. All the ingredients are present—actors, perceptions, diminishing space, and diminishing resources. Environmental mediation is a new technique to aid in solving the growing number of resource policy conflicts.

III.
Existing Aids for the Prospective Mediator

The prospective mediator need not approach environmental conflicts uninformed. Certain existing documents, techniques, and records supply insight into the parties and issues involved in various disputes. But how does one choose from the countless sources of information concerning the environment in general and specific environmental matters in particular? The mediator must be selective, choosing only the most valuable and useful information based on certain criteria.

CRITERIA FOR SELECTION OF EXISTING AIDS

1. Aids useful for identification of parties, issues or perceptions of the conflict.

   In order to learn about key factors pertaining to a situation under study, the mediator should give priority to those documents which identify parties, issues, or perceptions of the conflict. Environmental impact statements, management plans, and case law illustrate the materials that fit this category.

2. Aids useful for suggesting existing statutory bases from which mediation might begin or on which an agreement might be based.

An agreement negotiated outside a court of law must have some binding effect on the parties for effective implementation. If a lawsuit is filed, a legal basis for settlement exists. Case law, existing statutes, zoning, annexation and subdivision regulations, administrative agreements, or other legal and quasi-legal documents can assist the mediator in this category.

3. Aids useful for suggesting alternative and/or compromise solutions to a potential conflict.

Certain documents can and do suggest alternative solutions to a problem. Environmental impact statements and documents prepared in anticipation of the EIS (e.g., information papers listing management alternatives for recreational lands) sometimes contain upwards of five alternative proposals, ranging from no development to full development. Some documents may also contain an analysis of the conflicts generated by each alternative; a certain alternative is then selected which gives weight to this analysis. Well-placed resource persons may suggest further compromises or suggest that compromise is not desirable in a particular case.

EVALUATION OF ENVIRONMENTAL IMPACT

Federal and state laws require that most projects undertaken by public and private developers be regulated. The regulation may take the form of permits, licenses, approved environmental impact statements, or document filings with appropriate agencies. Of these, the EIS is most worthy of review by the prospective mediator. The EIS preparation, review, and comment process results in a final product which fits all three criteria mentioned above.

The EIS is required according to the provisions of the National Environmental Policy Act (PL 91-190, 42 U.S.C. 4321, *et seq.*), promulgated January 1, 1970. NEPA's oft-quoted section 102 (2)(C), which mandates that a detailed EIS be included "in every recommendation or report on proposals for legislation and other major Federal actions significantly affecting the quality of the human environment," has had far-reaching effects on the way our nation conducts its business.

Because of this provision and others like it at the state level, the prospective environmental mediator will often use the EIS or other assessments of environmental impact as background for a mediation case study.

Use of the EIS urges consideration of certain questions. First: What factors must an EIS contemplate? Second: How might one actually evaluate environmental impact once the factors are identified? Third: How effective is the EIS preparation, review, and comment process for identification of parties, issues, perceptions, conflicts, and alternative solutions?

The first two questions are obviously of least importance to this discussion and will be answered succinctly. In theory, the EIS must consider all relevant impacts of a proposed action. The statement must also discuss any unavoidable, adverse environmental effects, alternatives to the proposed action, the relationship between short-term environmental uses and maintenance and enhancement of long-term productivity, and any irreversible or irretrievable commitments of resources should a proposed action be implemented.

According to the Council on Environmental Quality (CEQ, 1973a), which developed guidelines for implementation of NEPA, secondary, indirect impacts must be considered in addition to primary impacts (38 Fed. Reg. 20550, *et seq.,* Aug. 1, 1973). A proposed winter recreation area EIS, for example, must also consider impacts on housing, transportation, social structure, and other services on private lands at the mountain base, in addition to primary impacts of the ski trails themselves, which are usually in public ownership.

An EIS is assembled according to procedures specifically designed to evaluate the environmental impact of a proposed action. Various schemes have been suggested for this purpose. In practice, the usual EIS is developed by a combination of techniques assessing the magnitude and importance of each impact, interactions between man and relevant ecosystems, and both quantitative and subjective measures. Different models have also been proposed for different resource problems.

Aside from faithfully adhering to its preparation technique, the EIS must meet certain procedural requirements. Section 1503 of the new CEQ guidelines for NEPA (1978) speaks of review of draft impact statements by federal, state, and local agencies, and by the general public. Summaries of reviewers' comments are then attached to the final statement according to the provisions of Section 1503.4 (b).

Analysis of attached comments may show the environmental statement to have obvious inadequacies. Further, comments reveal the evident biases which reveal the importance particular agencies or concerned individuals attach to certain impacts. Parties and issues are identified. Potential conflicts are also identified. Such parties, issues, and potential conflicts may be further delineated in the informational meetings and public hearings which accompany EIS preparation and review.

One draft EIS by the U.S. Forest Service (USFS) reveals a technique that promises to help the prospective mediator to a greater extent than does the normal impact analysis (U.S. Forest Service, 1976: 54-65). This document, prepared for the Boulder-Grand Divide Planning Unit in Colorado (BGD), includes the results of a special study performed by a Colorado State University researcher. The researcher (Freeman, 1976) conducted "A Social Well-Being Analysis of the Impacts of Four Management Alternatives for the Boulder-Grand Divide Planning Unit." One of the elements of the study was a ranking of each alternative as to degree of social conflict (relatively more or less polarization). This element of the study, although criticized in review by the State of Colorado (Lorenson, 1977), was commended for addressing the social impacts of USFS management proposals.

Use of Freeman's study for interalternative analysis and evaluation of the BGD alerts the mediator to polarizing alternatives and the issues which generate this polarization. Groups—whether ethnic, occupational, user, or otherwise—can then be identified in preparation for the mediation effort. The USFS is continuing the social well-being conflict analysis technique in preliminary documents on the Piedra Land Management Planning and Wild and Scenic River Study for southwest Colorado (U.S. Forest Service, 1977). The evaluation is based on principles and standards developed by the U.S. Water Resources Council (1976).

The EIS is an interdisciplinary analysis, with contributions from various disciplinary experts integrated into a team effort. Freeman's study, for example, is sociological in nature. Other studies utilizing the public participation process and determining the social desires of affected parties are quite common. Several states, for instance, have conducted critical resource identification and information programs: results of such programs can obviously be instructive to potential mediators.

Impacts of resource use have been assessed from other disciplinary perspectives. The economic benefit/cost analysis is familiar to students of environmental conflicts. Variations of the benefit/cost analysis can identify affected parties and estimate monetary amounts to be received by each party given a certain alternative (e.g., see Coberly-Manson, 1973). Conflicts might then be identified and minimized by the third party.

Political scientists have analyzed resource policy decisions from their disciplinary perspective. Dorfman and Jacoby (1971) proposed a mathematical model to predict the outcomes of a political decision process regarding a water pollution policy problem. One concept discussed in their study (and previously mentioned in this text) is *pareto admissibility*—i.e., some alternative will be more advantageous to some party than the existing alternative but will not cost (or injure) the other parties more than any other alternative. In other words, the net benefit to all parties is optimum. Again, a variation of the benefit/cost analysis, modified to political outcomes, can assist the prospective mediator.

The EIS process and other methods for assessment of environmental impact should nonetheless be used with caution. Critics of the EIS process have found fault with the "fill-in-the-blanks" approach used by many agencies after they have achieved a format and content style approved by CEQ and other reviewers. Certain assumptions and deficiencies in the EIS may be evident, maximizing or minimizing the importance of certain issues and conflicts. Some reviewers' comments may be consolidated into a "unified position," necessitating further research before technical or political conflicts are apparent.

Techniques for environmental assessment may also be lacking. Certain techniques have been considered too subjective, too complex, too simple, or lacking in analysis of secondary impacts; and secondary, indirect impacts are of special concern to the mediator. Proposed developments on public lands represent cases where adjacent developments on private lands may create major conflicts but may not be adequately addressed in the EIS analysis. No scheme is perfect—the prospective mediator should use these aids with full awareness of their imperfections.

ENVIRONMENTAL LEGISLATION AND LITIGATION

Environmental legislation, including the guidelines, standards, and procedures it requires, is often the focal point of an environmental dispute. A brief description of important environmental laws at the federal level and a sampling of similar state laws will support a discussion of these laws as aids to the mediator.

The *National Environmental Policy Act* (NEPA) of 1969 (42 U.S.C. 4321, *et seq.*) declares a national environmental policy, recognizes the responsibility of Congress toward the environment, and mandates that all policies, regulations, and public laws of the United States "shall be interpreted and administered in accordance with the policies set forth" in the Act (Section 102 (1)). NEPA also addresses, at 102 (2)(B), as previously quoted, the need for methods and procedures "which will insure that presently unquantified environmental amenities and values may be given appropriate consideration in decisionmaking along with economic and technical considerations..." Subsequent case law, to be discussed later in this section, interprets the language of Section 102 and illustrates the "balancing" technique (see *Environmental Law Reporter*, 1972). Consequently, a federal agency may have done much preliminary work for the mediator by balancing various considerations. If a conflict remains, further analysis and study of compromised, balanced positions may be desirable for promoting settlement.

The *Federal Water Pollution Control Act Amendments* (FWPCA) of 1972 (33 U.S.C. 1251, *et seq.*) have as their goals the installation of "best practicable" water treatment techniques at all facilities by 1977, "swimmable" standards in all streams by 1983, and "no discharge" by 1985. The basic regulatory requirements are that point source dischargers must obtain permits allowing only prescribed effluents at prescribed levels, and that schedules for compliance with standards as promulgated by the Environmental Protection Agency (EPA) be prepared and submitted. A citizen suit provision is also present. This provision allows citizens to initiate legal action against industries or EPA if, in the public view, standards are not being met. Variances from the standards, discharges as a health hazard, and debate over regulatory provisions of FWPCA (e.g., permits) versus economic alternatives to the law (e.g., effluent charges) are the major points of conflict which have arisen during implementation of the FWPCA (see Council on Environmental Quality, 1973b: 168-182).

The Clean Air Act Amendments (CAA) of 1970 (42 U.S.C. 1857, *et seq.*) provide a vigorous scheme for improvement of air quality standards throughout the nation. The legislation directly or indirectly affects energy policy, transportation planning, the auto industry, other heavy industry, and national land use policy. Primary responsibility is given to the states to establish air quality regions and to prepare implementation plans for achieving air quality standards. As with the FWPCA, much litigation has resulted from the civil suit provisions of the CAA. Conflicts have arisen primarily over standards and variances from these standards, approval of state implementation plans, the non-degradation policy and its effect on state and regional land use planning, and the economic impacts on the individual consumer of reducing auto pollution (see *Environmental Law Reporter*, 1973). Subsequent amendments to CAA have helped matters somewhat, but the law remains controversial and its implementation remains as elusive as the air it attempts to regulate.

The *Noise Control Act* of 1972 (42 U.S.C. 4901, *et seq.*) incorporates previous noise control legislation by regulating aircraft, railways, motor carriers, and products distributed in commerce. Under this Act, standards and guidelines with respect to noise pollution are promulgated by the EPA Administrator. Primary conflicts have arisen over the taking issue (generally defined as a "taking" of the use and enjoyment of property because of noise, odor, hazard, or other factors) near airports and railway lines.

Other important environmental conflicts have resulted from federal legislation on such varied topics as mineral leasing, dumping in rivers and harbors, wilderness preservation, administrative procedure in grants for road construction, and toxic substances. These conflicts and the laws each involve are too numerous and detailed to analyze here. It is clear that the record of environmental legislation at the federal level provides a broad and varied arena for application of the mediator's skills. Further, the applicable environmental laws often give the mediator a beginning point for his deliberations.

Many states have introduced environmental legislation dealing with specific aspects of pollution control and with environmental policy in general. Wisconsin's Environmental Policy Act is patterned closely after NEPA, and requires that an EIS by state agencies be included in every "recommendation or report on proposals for legislation and other major actions significantly affecting the quality of the human environment" (Wis. Stats., Sec. 1.11 (2) (C)). The EIS is subsequently reviewed by a division of the Wisconsin Department of Natural Resources.

In Michigan, a citizen suit provision is included in the state environmental protection act. Some 80 suits were filed under this provision by the end of 1973, most commonly over industrial air pollution and land development. DiMento (1975), in his analysis of the provision and the conflicts it has generated, has found that the citizen suit clause has not encouraged a mass exodus of industry. Citizens and public officials alike have benefitted from its streamlining effect on administrative proceedings and from the environmental education it provides.

The State of Colorado has taken a slightly different approach. Since the majority of Colorado citizens advocate local control of land use (Fisher, 1976: 9-10), the State has addressed regulation of land use through amendments to subdivision regulations (State of Colorado, 1972) and by allowing local governments to designate and regulate matters declared to be in the "state interest" (State of Colorado, 1974). The record of land use conflicts in Colorado shows that, as one might predict, air and water pollution issues are often involved.

Vermont and Illinois are among the other states which have passed legislation for environmental protection since 1970 (see Jaffe and Tribe, 1971: 678-701). As with their federal counterparts, state environmental laws have had varying degrees of success. These federal and state laws have nevertheless substantially changed the focus of the decisionmaking process. They have also generated case law which can help the prospective mediator more thoroughly identify parties, issues, conflicts, and compromises.

As indicated earlier, a complete discussion of pertinent case law would consume several chapters. Nevertheless, a few examples will serve to illustrate the use of case law as an aid to mediation efforts.

From the mediator's perspective, some of the most instructive environmental case law interprets NEPA. The balancing of opposing considerations required by the law is supported in opinions from landmark environmental lawsuits *(Environmental Law Reporter,* 1973a: 50034). NEPA is interpreted to mandate a finely-tuned, systematic balancing process which attempts to weigh environmental costs and risks against economic, technical, or social benefits of a project.

The memorandum and order issued following judgment on the Wallisville (Trinity River) Project in Texas, as proposed by the U.S. Army Corps of Engineers, provides detailed analysis on the topic of quantifying selected environmental amenities *(Sierra Club v. Froelke,* 1973). Benefit/cost procedures are evaluated and criticized in depth in this decision. In fact, questionable costs computations and assigned benefits were the major reasons for issuance of an injunction against the project. The Court also states (p. 1370) that "a favorable benefit/cost ratio combining all facets of a project must represent the final synthesis of technical, economic, and environmental factors."

Case law can obviously aid the mediator by listing principal parties, identifying key issues, and highlighting conflicts. On another level, case law may show an attempt to balance competing interests. If a conflict remains in the form of an appeal or motion of some sort, relevant case law can serve as a starting point for the conciliation effort.

ADMINISTRATIVE PROCEDURE

Environmental laws at the federal level are administered according to regulations, guidelines, rules, and administrative procedures promulgated by the responsible agency. Federal agency decisions on environmental matters (which embody the administration of environmental laws) are reviewed according to the standard of Section 706 of the Administrative Procedure Act (APA), 5 U.S.C. 706 (Supp. V). Various other tests are contained in case law or other statutes and regulations predating NEPA; these tests discuss criteria for choosing alternatives based on environmental impact (see *Environmental Law Reporter,* 1973a: 50026, 50035-50036; *Hanly v. Kleindienst,* 1972). However, the general court review provision is contained in the APA as cited above—to the layman, commonly termed the "arbitrary and capricious" standard.

Administrative hearings conducted by an administrative law judge or hearing officer can be an important source of information for the prospective mediator. By way of explanation, the function of an administrative law judge is established by statute in the organic act for a particular commission or agency (e.g., for the National Transportation Safety Board, see 49 U.S.C.A. 1902). Administrative hearings, also established by statute, are quasi-judicial in nature and provide a record of testimony, appearances, and findings which identifies parties and issues in a trial. The administrative hearing concerns administrative actions of an agency, such as issuance of permits. If a potential dispute exists over a decision which has been or will be made, the hearing record can aid the mediator in the manner previously indicated. If a party challenges the aforementioned decision in court under standards established in the APA, the trial record will provide additional information.

Parties in appearance at administrative or rule-making hearings and in public hearings of other types may represent an interesting cross-section for consideration by the mediator. An instructive analysis is suggested by one prominent environmental mediator, Cormick (1977), regarding the responsibilities and constraints of various parties in appearance. Cormick suggests the following categories:

(1) agencies who are required by law or administrative rules to comment, provide expert testimony, or otherwise state an opinion on the matter;

(2) environmental, citizen, and public interest group representatives, who comment voluntarily in the public interest (often because of personal interests);

(3) agencies, mostly at the regional and state levels, which have specific regulatory responsibilities and are therefore constrained from a range of actions regarding the matter, i.e., they are required by statute or regulation to advocate a specific position; and

(4) agencies, mostly at the state and federal level, which have specific constraints but also have broader policy goals as mandated by legislation.

Agencies at (4) may have policy and regulatory conflicts which make it doubly difficult to adopt a consistent position.

The mediator must recognize the responsibilities and constraints on agencies as they administer rules and regulations. The sanctions on each party to a conflict determine that party's posture to a large extent. It follows that the potential mediability of a dispute can be influenced by administrative and regulatory constraints or by lack of such constraints.

MEDIATION IN EXISTING LEGAL OR ADMINISTRATIVE ARRANGEMENTS

This section will discuss existing, informal efforts by various individuals, groups, or agencies which are not to be termed "environmental mediation" (as discussed in the following chapters) but which will be instructive to the prospective mediator. These existing efforts would aptly fit the first and second criteria at the beginning of this chapter: aids useful for identifying parties, issues, or perceptions of the conflict, or those useful for suggesting existing statutory bases from which mediation might begin.

Evidence that federal agency officials have the discretion to mediate is not prominent. Such evidence is found in some interpretations and language, however. Figure 2 gives examples of salient language or procedures from legislation, case law, or other administrative arrangements that might be broadly defined as mediation. It should be noted that mediation is most applicable during the administration (or implementation) of relevant statutes.

Further study is suggested by several of the examples in Figure 2. Mediable aspects of the Clean Air Act, for instance, are now being investigated by Manko (1976) in his work for the University City Science Center in Philadelphia. And Jane McCarthy (1977), now working in New York City, has met with CEQ representatives regarding a mediation function for that Council.

The interstate water pollution control conference was a type of formal information/hearing proceeding that could aid a concurrent mediation effort. Section 10 of the 1956 FWPCA (Fig. 2) appears to provide for some implementation and enforcement of conference findings. The procedure has since been deleted from the water pollution control legislation, but is still present, to my knowledge, in the Clean Air Act amendments.

Figure 2 also shows mediable aspects of litigation and of two attempts to resolve disputes involving surface water and ocean resources. Similar recent efforts more closely tied to environmental mediation will be discussed in the following chapters, as will the technical terms used in Figure 2.

Other scattered evidence suggests a concern for third party intervention in disputes over use of natural resources. Opponents of federal estuarine programs, by which estuarine sanctuaries would be acquired under Section 312 of the Coastal Management Act of 1972, feared there would be no "final arbiter" between the government and public over permit requirements for use of such sanctuaries (Zile, 1974: 250). Zoning boards of appeal may be said to act as arbitrators between the private and public interest in conflicts over land use (Council of State Governments, 1974: 13). Implementation of state laws such as Wisconsin's shoreland zoning statute (Wis. Stats., Sec. 59.971 and 144.26) could be viewed as a mediation effort between the state and public.

Legal or Administrative Arrangement	Reference	Clues to Mediable Aspects	Salient features
1. NEPA, PL 91-190 1Jan70	42 U.S.C. 4321, *et seq.*	CEQ guidelines, 38 Fed. Reg. 20550, *et seq.* 1Aug73, Secs. 1500.9-1500.11	EIS preparation and review; arrival at satisfactory statement before project initiation; application of environmental goals to exisiting programs; balancing of environmental costs with technical, economic, and social benefits
2. FWPCA, PL 84-660 1956 (now superseded by 3)		Interstate water pollution conference procedure, Sec. 10	Definition of parties by mediator; formal mediation sessions concurrent with conference
3. FPWCA, PL 92-500 18Oct72	33 U.S.C. 1251, *et seq.*	Water quality related effluent limitations, Sec. 302 (b) (2) "...and the Administration shall adjust such limitation as it applies to each person."	Variances; discharge as a health hazard; alternate disposal methods; economic v. regulatory schemes for pollution control; administrative orders
4. CAA, PL 91-604 1970	42 U.S.C. 1857, *et seq.*	Enforcement by Administrator, Sec. 113; inspections and monitoring, Sec. 114; interstate air pollution conference procedure, Sec. 115	Nondegradation policy; standards regarding autos and energy supplies; acceptance of state implementation plans; consent decree and implementation schedule; administrative orders

Fig. 2. Existing legal or administrative arrangements bearing on mediation.

(continued)

Fig. 2 continued

Legal or Administrative Arrangement	Reference	Clues to Mediable Aspects	Salient features
5. Coastal Zone Management Act. PL 92-583 27Oct72	86 Stat. 1280. *et seq.*	In case of disagreement over state mgmt. plans. Sec. of Commerce, with assistance of Exec. Off. of Pres., will "seek to mediate the differences," Sec. 307(b)	Definition of successful and unsuccessful events in which Secretary attempted mediation
6. All litigation	Karan, 1961 (see references)	Withdrawal of suit after being filed (with consent of parties)	Stipulation for dismissal, stipulation, and order for dismissal with prejudice as part of court record
7. Disputes over water allocation	Karan, 1961 (see references)	Water master appointed by court to sift issues and recommend decision to U.S. Supreme Court on major interstate conflicts over water allocation	Study of time, expense, and usefulness of this function; study water referees of other types
8. Disputes over U.S. outer continental shelf seabed and subsoil resources	*Coastal Zone Management Newsletter*, 1975 (see references)	Special Master appointed to review disputes between federal and state govts. and to make recommendations	Study record as with water master

Another mediatory aspect of Wisconsin's government is the role of the Public Intervenor, an assistant attorney general from the Justice Department who represents "the public rights" in hearings or proceedings on resource matters. In the summer of 1978, the Public Intervenor was involved in a successful mediation effort over the location, construction, and operation of a sanitary landfill. The Environmental Mediation Project of the Wisconsin Center for Public Policy conducted the mediation, but the Public Intervenor acted as catalyst to promote their involvement (Busterud and Vaughn, 1979; also see appendix, page 183.)

As each resource dispute gains prominence it becomes the subject of much debate, study, and analysis. The prospective mediator must first gain use of all prior information on the topic and decide whether to discard it, use it in part, or study it thoroughly. Second, he must be aware of the relevant administrative and legal requirements. Finally, prior covert (informal) or overt mediation attempts must be analyzed. These three steps are important preliminaries if mediation is to be attempted. Use of existing aids will help the mediator to establish an advanced starting point for his efforts.

IV.
The Mediation Function

The mediation function is familiar to many of us through its application to labor and community disputes in the public and in the private sector. Teacher strikes, walk-outs at local industrial or commercial establishments, rent strikes, strikes of state employees, and demonstrations by university students have all been mediated in recent decades. Sometimes the mediator is unsuccessful. Often, however, opponents do agree to settlement with the help of a third party. The compromise frequently seems a miraculous, speedy stroke of genius by one or a few mediators, who enter and leave the conflict without much attention. What exactly does mediation involve? Why has mediation shown itself to be more applicable to site-specific environmental disputes than the other levels of third party intervention? Can the techniques and theories of third party intervention in labor and community disputes be effectively transferred to environmental conflicts? How does mediation compare to litigation for resolution of environmental disputes? Finally, what are some social and psychological aspects of human relationships that the mediator should consider as he tries to promote compromise?

MEDIATION DEFINED

Mediation can perhaps be best defined by a comparison with the other levels of impartial third party intervention in disputes. The following levels of third party intervention come from a labor relations context. According to Simkin (1971: 25-26), there are six levels of intervention (Fig. 3). *Conciliation* is the mildest form, characterized by the "good guy" who tries to make things run smoothly and keep the parties talking. *Mediation* is slightly more aggressive. The mediator may make suggestions or (rarely) procedural recommendations, but has no power or authority to settle disputes. *Fact-finding* constitutes the next level; it is a "masterful analysis of statistics, arguments, and contentions," so skillfully presented that the way to settlement is clear. *Fact-finding with recommendations* makes the analysis and presents a specific recipe for settlement.

All the above forms of intervention imply no obligation to the disputants, who may accept or reject the third party's suggestions (if indeed any are made) as they wish. (Note: As used in this text, *intervention* and *intervenor* will mean informal action by an impartial third party, unless legal intervention is specified.)

To illustrate the dramatic impact which these more voluntary, passive forms of intervention might have, we may consider the Madison, Wisconsin teacher's strike of 1975-1976 (Feldman, 1976). Talks for a new 1976 contract began in June, 1975. Mediation was requested in early October, 1975, and began October 9th. A fact-finder was requested on December 5, 1975. After approximately 90 days of mediation with infrequent formal sessions, the fact-finder arrived on January 13, 1976. The contract was ratified on Saturday, January 17th, and teachers returned to work the following Monday, only six days after the fact-finder arrived! The Madison experience was perhaps exceptional: a fortunate combination of the proper function introduced at the critical stage of an appropriate dispute. It does, however, illustrate the speed with which the more passive forms of intervention may take effect.

Two more active forms of third party intervention are shown on Fig. 3. Simkin describes *voluntary arbitration* as "fact-finding plus," since the arbitrator's decision holds because of his fact-finding knowledge. The parties recognize this knowledge when they volunteer to submit to binding arbitra-

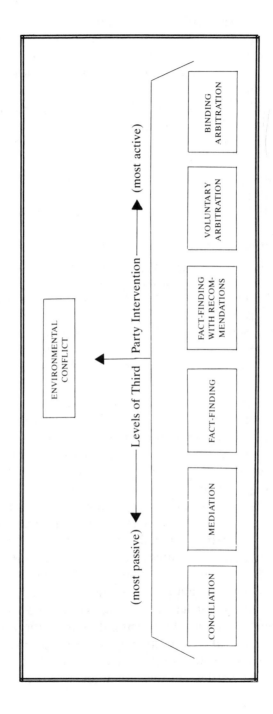

Fig. 3.   **Levels of third-party intervention as applied to environmental conflict. (adopted from Simkin, 1971)**

tion. *Compulsory arbitration* by individuals, a board, or a court is imposed on a union, company, or industry, usually by government, to eliminate a crippling strike. Steelworkers and automakers have been subject to such arbitration repeatedly.

Mediation is that level of intervention often most suitable to site-specific environmental disputes. Precise definition of the term and technique of mediation followed by some discussion of its use in other dispute areas will illustrate this point.

Simkin (1971: 358) defines mediation as non-repressive assistance in problem-solving. This problem-solving is accomplished *by* the conflicting parties (not *for* them) with help from the mediator.

Mediation is "the process by which a third party who is acceptable to all the conflicting parties *helps them* in reaching a mutually satisfactory settlement of differences" (emphasis added). The mediator is a facilitator who aids in settlement but who has no power, in the traditional sense of the word, to dictate settlement. For purposes of immediate discussion, *mediation is defined as voluntary, fairly inactive, informal third party intervention, which assists in rather than forces settlement between conflicting parties.*

Several phrases in the preceding paragraph show why mediation, according to Simkin's levels of intervention, is most appropriate for environmental conflict. Environmental disputes often demand a catalyst, a third party who can help parties reach compromise. A slightly more active role than conciliation is needed. But if the intervenor becomes a fact-finder or even an arbitrator, he loses effectiveness. The complexity of environmental disputes, involving diverse parties, interests, goals, and settlements, demands that the parties be committed to the negotiations. They must feel it is *their* dispute, that they are negotiating on *their* terms, and that *their* ideas are part of the compromise. The nature of the mediated settlement—politically but often not legally binding, according to Cormick (1977)—requires a good-faith commitment by the disputants. If the intervenor takes too active a role by proposing solutions and selling his ideas too strongly, parties may lose their commitment to the settlement and abandon it at the first sign of stress.

MEDIATION IN LABOR AND COMMUNITY DISPUTES

Mediation has established itself as a useful technique in labor conflicts. University courses are taught on labor-management relations, a substantial literature exists, and theory is well-documented. The following discussion will compare aspects of other dispute management areas to those involving environmental issues.

A newer but nonetheless widely accepted use of mediation is in the area of community disputes. Several researchers, including those at the Institute of Mediation and Conflict Resolution, the National Center for Dispute Settlement of the American Arbitration Association (both in New York City), and the Community Crisis Intervention Center of Washington University in St. Louis, have tested mediation techniques under simulated and real-life situations. The researchers found that many techniques used in labor negotiations do indeed transfer to community disputes.

Critics of the transferability notion argue that the community dispute implies a determination of what is "right": a search for truth. This determination is in contrast to the determination of what is "fair" in labor-management negotiations over such economic issues as wages, vacation benefits, and pensions. Proponents of transferability reply that the mediator's view of the settlement is not important; the parties are negotiating, and their views are foremost in order for a satisfactory resolution (Nicolau and Cormick, 1972: 98-99). Since community disputes involve issues that are often negotiable (e.g., rents, living conditions, university regulations), theory from labor-management conflict is applicable.

Community disputes are familiar situations to many of us. The issues are often explosive, affecting not only the workplace, but the very fabric of society. Examples of disputes that have been mediated are those between landlords and tenants, administrators and students, merchants and consumers, clients and agencies, and racial groups (*Crisis and Change,* 1972; Kaye, 1971).

Because one group in community conflict is usually the "out" group, the intervenor may at one time or another play the role of community activist, advocate, mediator, enforcer, or a combination of two or more roles while attempting to facilitate a settlement. These supplemental roles involve training and organization of the "out" group, promotion of goals, and possible enforcement of the settlement after it occurs (*Crisis and Change,* 1972: 2).

Saul Alinsky (1969; 1971) has written much on the theory of organization of radical groups in conflict with established economic or political interests. Indeed, he believes that "a free and open society is an on-going conflict, interrupted periodically by compromises" (Alinsky, 1971: 59). Consultation of Alinsky's works and those of the various dispute resolution centers previously mentioned will provide further background on community dispute case studies for the interested reader.

The literature shows some direct connections between labor disputes and environmental factors. One writer has suggested that labor unions should bargain to improve their working environment regarding air pollution (Murphy, 1971). Others (California Law Revision Commission, 1971) urge enactment of regulations allowing arbitration on just compensation, a subject which has been treated in environmental litigation. But the most obvious and valid extension of techniques for dispute settlement to the environment comes from the literature on community disputes.

As an example, one researcher with first-hand experience notes that the timing of intervention is important in both dispute types. It follows that the parties both in community and in environmental disputes must clearly visualize their goals and the ways to achieve these goals. Mediation allows parties to sit down, explore their differences, and perhaps for the first time really communicate with one another (McCarthy, 1974).

Other similarities exist among labor, community, and environmental disputes, as noted in Fig. 4. Dissimilarities are also shown. Theory is notably lacking for the analysis of environmental conflict, probably because this is a new field. The components of labor disputes are well-defined as a result of many years of bargaining. Components of community and environmental conflict show progressively less definition.

Consideration of the issues column of Fig. 4 may be instructive. Issues in labor conflict are well-defined and narrow:

they concern only employment relations and the economic distribution of wages and benefits. Externalities, or indirect impacts of the settlement, may indicate the need for a third party to be assigned to expedite settlement—e.g., a crippling, nationwide coal workers' strike may prompt compulsory arbitration imposed by government.

The community dispute often has recognized geographic boundaries for groups and affected areas. Usually the dispute itself is over externalities, such as the impact of new university regulations on minority students. Though the conflict is over externalities, disputants share a common area (neighborhood, city, campus) and desire peace in that area.

At first glance, environmental disputes appear to lack either of the defining traits of labor and community conflicts. But environmental disputes frequently: involve externalities, can be defined geographically, and include economic issues.

DISPUTE TYPES

		Labor	Community	Environmental
	Setting	Well defined, although national implications of settlement may be difficult to perceive	Usually well defined, but again, implications of settlement may be difficult to perceive at national level	Often not well defined, because of varying scales of conflict, settlement, and influence
DISPUTE COMPONENTS	Parties	Well defined	Usually well defined, but weaker may need definition (e.g., groups of renters); endorsed representatives may be difficult to locate	Usually not well defined; representatives of certain groups may be difficult to identify
	Power of Parties	Well defined from past practices	One side may be well defined; mediator/advocate may have to provide educational or organizational function for other	Same as community disputes
	Issues	Well defined and narrow; concern only employment relations	Usually well defined; lack of definition involving externalities; common geographic area	May be complex, involving externalities, economic factors, and varying geographic areas; need definition and clarification in most cases
	Outcomes and Their Effects	Generally predictable (new contract or strike); sometimes a far-reaching impact	Changes may be clear, but often have indirect impacts	Much redistribution can occur in resources, income, or power; outcome may produce confusing results

NOTE: Components adapted from: Community Crisis Intervention Center, 1972. Case study outline (mimeo). Washington University, St. Louis, Mo, 4 pp.

Fig. 4. **Parallels in labor, community, and environmental disputes.**

The jobs versus environment conflict is increasingly common as health hazards are discovered in the man-influenced environment. Working and living conditions, health hazards, and environmental pollution draw together labor, community, and environmental disputes while indicating common application of settlement techniques. Proponents of environmental mediation believe that the carry-over from labor to community to environmental disputes is realistic.

MEDIATION AND LITIGATION

While considering mediation for the resolution of environmental conflict, alternatives should also be considered. The most prominent alternative is litigation. Litigation of conflicts relating to environmental quality took place almost one hundred years ago (see *Baltimore and Potomac Railroad Company v. Fifth Baptist Church*, 1883). However, most environmental litigation has followed promulgation of the National Environmental Policy Act and other federal laws on air and water pollution. Litigation of environmental conflicts would seem to be the only reasonable alternative to mediation (representing out-of-court conflict resolution in general) for settlement using a third party. The question is whether court sanction is a necessary and desirable means for resolving the conflict. Indeed, there are circumstances in which litigation is not a rational option (Cormick, 1973: 5) and mediation is the only possible course. The opposite is also true.

In some respects, litigation would seem to offer several advantages over mediation:

(1) Litigation is a recognized public process.
The courtroom is an established forum for resolution of differences in our society. Judges, lawyers, and juries are traditional and generally respected as means for implementing the public good. And significantly, the court settlement is legal and binding on parties, pending appeal, and is enforced by the police power of the state.

(2) Litigation serves to focus public attention on important issues.

Lawsuits frequently call attention to issues that are of far-reaching public importance. Civil suit provisions in some laws allow the citizen to become directly involved by bringing government agencies to court (*Resources*, 1971: 809). National television and other news media coverage allows the public to follow a case and become informed about the outcome. In the environmental arena, cases such as the Reserve Mining Company in Minnesota (*U.S. v. Reserve Mining*, 1974a) have helped to define the economy/environment dilemma. By comparison, mediation is less visible than litigation and generates less media interest.

(3) Litigation serves to improve the regulatory, administrative, and legislative process.

Litigation often reveals inadequacies in regulatory agencies through an exposure of their workings. Administrative procedure may be streamlined and improved because of legal findings and judicial direction, or consequent executive order. The courts have also construed the legal provisions of environmental law in such a manner as to find solutions to environmental problems before the legislature does (*Conservation Foundation Newsletter*, 1969: 3). As previously mentioned, the procedural aspects of NEPA have been defined extensively by the courts. The courts have definitely aided the cause of non-legal techniques for settlement of environmental disputes by defining the issues, establishing credibility, power, and recognition for interest groups, and refining procedure. Preservationists, developers, and those in-between know where they stand, what is expected of them, and what pressures they may be subjected to in the future.

What then are the advantages of mediation over litigation? How can mediation be compared with the time-honored, authoritative tradition of the American judicial system?

(1) Mediation is as speedy as the parties wish it to be.

If mediation services are readily available, the parties may choose to begin negotiations immediately. The speedy due process provided by mediation is in contrast to the congestion in the courts (Fall, 1972). A court may inadvertently delay settlement for months and even years, because of a backlog of cases and the time requirements of legal procedure. Former Supreme Court Justice Frankfurter (quoted in Coulson, 1973: 8) stated that arbitration (representing out-of-court intervention) has the advantage "of providing a speedier, more economic, and more effective enforcement than can be had by the tortuous course of litigation." Frankfurter's words lead us to other advantages of the mediation process.

(2) Mediation is less expensive than litigation. A mediated settlement would involve perhaps one-half the cost of a similar, litigated one.

Lawsuits involve numerous expenses, including drafting of complaints, motions and interrogatories, the filing of depositions, and the actual trial appearance. Appeals, of course, can double or triple the cost. Even the simplest environmental lawsuit was estimated to cost from $1,125-$3,375 in 1974. Cases involving expert witnesses or several days of testimony may run much higher (Reitze and Reitze, 1974).

The mediation effort would certainly involve many of the same research expenses and interviews with members of the disputing parties. Overhead would be less than that for the lawsuit, however. A mediated settlement would require a set of two or more meeting rooms for negotiating sessions and individual party caucuses, compensation for the mediator of $200-$250/day, duplicating and other material costs, and any special costs (e.g., on-site inspections, computer expenses) of the particular settlement. It appears that, even with a liberal allowance for expenses, the simplest mediated settlement might cost no more than $800-$1000. Complicated, long-standing disputes which involve broad issues would of course involve substantial fees. Establishing credibility with the parties, performing detailed, original research, interviewing splinter groups with an interest in the settlement, and timing intervention properly may add up to thousands of dollars in mediation expenses and to many months of work. By comparison, a few complex environmental lawsuits have involved several years of litigation and millions of dollars in expenses.

(3) Mediation provides for flexibility and directness, because it is free of the often restrictive requirements of legal procedure.

During the mediation session, opponents discuss the real, immediate issues of the case. Plaintiffs and defendants are not designated, and plaintiffs accordingly need not find a litigable issue in order to resolve the major issue at hand. In *Wilderness Society v. Morton* (1973), for example, pipeline right-of-way was the issue litigated, while the real question was construction of the vast Alaska oil pipeline. As another example, an issue such as aesthetics may be debated in the negotiation/mediation session, while such a topic has generally been too subjective and "frivolous" for most courts to consider (Leighty, 1971: 1347).

Moreover, the adversary proceedings in the courtroom often force parties to take extreme positions, causing them to be viewed as unreasonable by the general public. During mediation, an extreme position need not be assumed (Cormick, 1973: 4-5).

Technical data and expert witnesses are easily dealt with by the mediator. He may act to sort out applicable information and input from experts and arrange for computer time, particular field studies, or other technical help. The parade of expert witnesses, with those hired by petitioner attempting to discredit those hired by respondent and vice versa, need not and perhaps should not be present in the mediation proceeding.

(4) Mediation is voluntary and usually leads to better enforcement precisely because the mediator has no power to enforce the decision. Curiously, the mediated decision may have a binding effect because of the "no power" bargaining situation.

Those who work with arbitration/mediation in labor relations and community disputes note the voluntary nature of third-party functions. Mediation especially remains voluntary because any party can reject the mediator at any time, and because the process relies on the willingness of each party to negotiate "in good faith" (Cormick, 1973: 2). The quoted phrase is borrowed from rules governing labor/management negotiations (see, e.g., *Wis. Stats.* Section 111.70 (1)(d)), and implies a mutual obligation on each party to bargain at reasonable times and in honest fashion toward a constructive settlement.

Even if parties to an environmental conflict agree to submit to arbitration, labor relations texts state that arbitration, too, is a *voluntary* process. The final determination by the arbitrator as to the rights of the parties has caused some to believe that the process is a compulsory one (Fall, 1972: 16). It is stressed, however, that the parties willingly agree to put their fate in the hands of the arbitrator and, in voluntary arbitration, cannot be coerced to do so.

The voluntary nature of third party intervention would seem to make the mediated settlement a lasting one. The parties are negotiating an agreement in *their* terms over *their* issues. The mediator merely facilitates this agreement; his view of settlement is not important and may not even be apparent. Certainly he may make suggestions when he sees a logical point of compromise, but these suggestions may be ignored. Moreover, any settlement may well need modification in the future on account of changing conditions. In this case, established past practices can be relied upon to quickly modify the agreement.

In summary, mediation is a worthy vehicle for resolution of environmental conflict. The attributes of due process, moderate expense, debate of real issues, and of informal voluntary procedure are all present.

SOCIAL AND PSYCHOLOGICAL
ASPECTS OF MEDIATION

The literature of sociology and psychology contains numerous works which discuss the conflict situation. Observations by experimental social psychologists and other researchers are useful to anyone dealing with human beings in disagreement. This section will attempt to identify various social and psychological aspects of individual and group interaction which might apply to environmental conflict.

- The nature of conflict and the negotiating group as a whole.

The nature of conflict itself has been explored over many years. On the one hand, conflict has been labeled as undesirable discord, and therefore a disruption in the harmony of man and nature. But Georg Simmel (1955) and Lewis Coser (1956; 1967) view *conflict as an instrument of social integration.* In this sense, conflict tends to act in a group-binding and group-preserving capacity. Conflict maintains, rather than disrupts, the well-balanced society by facilitating communication and defining relationships and group structures, so as to clarify for a participant his position and status relative to others. And, although conflict itself does not always take place within specified norms and rules, other types of interaction may take place, initiated by conflict, which follow specific, accepted procedures. Dialogue may be initiated that leads to settlement (Coser, 1956: 121-128). It follows that conflict and the ensuing settlement establish and maintain the balance of power, so that a legitimate distribution of resources is achieved. Parties perceive themselves *in equilibrium*—a condition that is the desired end of most conflict situations.

Formation of *coalitions* is a functional rather than a dysfunctional aspect of the conflict situation. The environmental mediator must pay particular attention to which groups are inclined toward preservation and which favor development. Ingram (1969: 14-16), in her instructive case study of the Colorado River Basin legislation, notes that the developers in that case relied on the process of consent-building and the social conventions of courtesy, reciprocity, and bargaining to achieve their ends. Support was built up over many months, until a local, basin-wide, and regional consensus was attained between development interests and politicians.

The preservationists in this case study resisted the proposed development. Local environmental groups distinctly opposed the project, while national organizations such as the Wilderness Society opposed a portion of the project because it threatened their core interest. Entrance of the environmentalist coalition into the dispute disrupted the carefully laid plans and delicate negotiations of the developers (Ingram, 1969: 70-71, 86-87). The preservationists used a massive publicity campaign, filled with what some called "scare tactics," to provoke an emotional response from the developers. The preservationist coalition seemed to build overnight a strength great enough to undermine what the developers had taken months and even years to achieve.

Conflict might be seen as functional because of the coalitions it creates and the flow of communication that results. The group-binding and group-preserving capacity should not be viewed as disruptive to the developers in the aforementioned example (even though *their* coalition was weakened) but as a natural function of society in maintaining the balance of power and in achieving equilibrium.

In general, it may be said that conflict is necessary before a third party can consider intervention. This statement may be obvious in the sense that the mediator must have something to mediate, but not so obvious in the sense that conflict is often desired and even welcomed by the groups involved. A show of strength allows each party to assess its position, regroup and reinforce if necessary, shore up its weaknesses and go on, hopefully with new spirit and vigor (Coser, 1956). In such cases, the mediator might be wise to let the dispute continue until it "ripens" before he intervenes.

The *time-cycle* and *ritual* connected with a conflict often play important roles in settlement efforts. Conflict situations typically display a ritual of inquiry, contact, negotiation, and (sometimes) settlement. Each phase takes an unspecified but usually substantial number of weeks or even months. The full time-cycle may take one or more years. Environmental disputes frequently do involve several years from initial disagreement—over whether a dam should be built, whether industry should be allowed to dispose of its wastes in a certain fashion, or whether a highway should pass through a park—to final resolution to the satisfaction of the majority (see, e.g., *Sierra Club v. Froehlke,* 1973). In between are protests by individuals or citizen action groups, intervention by national environmental groups, involvement of local, state, and federal agencies, initial, obviously inflated offers, courtrooms and expert witnesses, dramatic floods, accidents, media coverage, and other curious combinations of events.

Boulding (1962: 318) has described the ritualistic succession of events in some detail. The weaker party suggests opening negotiations, is recognized by the stronger party, and negotiations begin. Recognition and negotiations may be facilitated through advocacy by a third party to establish the legitimacy of the weaker party. During negotiations, parties make initial offers which they know are unreasonable, and concessions are made in later meetings. Traditionally, each party publicizes the magnitude of its concessions and the sincerity of its desire for settlement. Finally, often under time pressure, a settlement may be reached.

The mediator must keep in mind that the initial, often unreasonable offers which may open the negotiations are not unusual. A compromise reduction in demands by one (or both) sides may mean attainment of the actual objective. In private caucus, the mediator may explore what objective, for each side, is the so-called "bottom line" or "hidden agenda." If both sides have a "bottom line" which is similar, all the better. If one or both sides will not reduce the demands from the original position, or if the "bottom lines" are far apart, mediation must continue. Protracted negotiations with no sign of compromise indicate a dispute not suitable (or not *yet* suitable) for mediation.

The fact that this ritual is necessary and desired by the parties is validated by its repeated occurrence in all conflict situations. Referring back to the labor/community/environmental dispute diagrams (Fig. 4), we may note that the ritual is familiar to students of labor relations, that Cohen (1972: 2, 5) has identified a similar ritual of stages in the definition of community crisis, and that Cormick and McCarthy (1974) describe a comparable succession of events in an environmental dispute. Political and international conflict may follow a similar pattern.

The mediator consequently must determine the *timing of intervention*. An intervention early in the cycle might provide the best opportunity for a speedy settlement, or might be premature and cause negotiations to break off altogether. Taylor (1970: 12) has suggested that mediators in community disputes intervene in the final stages of disputes in the private sector and in middle or earlier stages for those in the public sector. No general pattern has yet been established for environmental disputes, although Cormick and McCarthy report intervention in what could be considered the later stages of conflict.

Intervention in later stages would imply few problems in recognizing established groups and forming a representative group for negotiations. However, even after several years of conflict it may be difficult to gather truly "representative" and sanctioned representatives. In any case, a detailed chronology of the dispute under consideration should be constructed, and much attention should be paid to the timing of intervention.

● The negotiating group as a collection of individuals.

After the intervenor studies how the groups come to form and ally themselves with one side or another, he may look to the groups themselves and their individual components. Much work has been done in experimental social psychology to determine how group behavior differs from individual behavior. Some of the most relevant topics will be discussed here as background to the mediation function.

Experimental work in group interaction is likely to produce conflicting results, but is instructive to the prospective intervenor. The *risk shift* phenomenon has received much attention. Risk shift studies have attempted to define whether persons acting in groups tend to take more risks than those same persons would take as individuals when confronted with similar, hypothetical situations in vocational choice, gambling, or investing money. In other words, the studies concern whether the tendency to take risks *shifts* to a higher or lower level in comparison of group and individual preferences. Initial studies indicated that groups tend to be more risky than individuals. Later studies disputed this theory by concluding that groups tend to reinforce conservative tendencies (see, e.g., Brown, 1974). Because the relationship between risk shift and compromise tendencies is unclear, it is difficult to relate risk shift to natural resource decisions such as floodplain zoning (Heberlein, 1976).

Myers and Lamm (1975) believe that *group discussion tends to polarize opinion.* The average prediscussion tendency (either to take risks or not) is enhanced, they believe, when one compares himself with the other group members, shares information, and is perhaps influenced by a leader with extreme views. Again, the relationship to compromise tendencies is cloudy, but individual interviews might give the mediator a key to positions after groups and coalitions are formed.

Composition of the group may be a factor in settlement. In one experiment (Hermann and Kogan, 1968), groups composed of leaders and those composed of persons with delegated authority reached settlement in different fashions. The latter type took extreme (either very long or very short) amounts of time to reach settlement, and were prone to compromise. Leaders, on the other hand, took a moderate but more consistent amount of time than delegates and tended to favor one position over another rather than a compromise.

Mediators can regulate the pace of negotiations and eliminate unnecessary ritual by helping individuals to have accurate *prenegotiation expectations.* In experimental situations, those negotiators with high levels of expectation received more favorable settlements for their side than did negotiators with lower expectations (Holmes, Throop, and Strickland, 1971). This research would seem to suggest that weaker, less organized groups in an environmental dispute should aim high and expect to fall short. Moreover, by assuring accurate prenegotiation expectations, the mediator could eliminate unrealistic goals which might be preventing the stronger party from even recognizing the weaker.

Once negotiations begin, *perceived firmness of the opponent* influences settlement. Podell and Knapp (1969) believe that mediation facilitates settlement by allowing the parties to make concessions through the mediator while maintaining a firm, strong front to opponents. One recognized characteristic of bargaining situations is that, once a party makes an obvious concession, the party holding firm will push and push until further concessions are made. The apparent weakness of the conceding party is exploited. I can confirm the efficiency of this tactic from personal experience in mock labor/management negotiations.

A mediator may provide an opportunity for *face-saving* by one or more parties. A negotiating team which experiences a serious loss of face in full view of opponents is often withdrawn, emotionally handicapped for further effective negotiation, and therefore polarized (Brown, 1968; 1970). The mediator can test potentially embarrassing but possibly fruitful suggestions by allowing parties to present the suggestions to him in private caucus, or by proposing them himself during negotiating sessions. The mediator may lose face, but the parties retain their relative strengths and bargaining is unimpeded.

There are undoubtedly several other social and psychological aspects of mediation which could be studied by the prospective intervenor. Some researchers have looked at such topics as the effects of time pressure and the opponent's concession rate on behavior in negotiation (Pruitt and Andrews, 1969) and the effects of being observed by partners of higher or lower status (Kogan, Lamm, and Trommsdorff, 1972). The general topic has potential for further research, especially as it concerns compromise and natural resource decisions.

- Some observations on larger scales—communities, ethnic groups, and nations.

Conflict may be viewed on a larger scale as a generator of community involvement and controversy. As such, it may be divisive, especially in small communities. The environmental dispute nicely fits the qualifications that Coleman (1957: 4-7) has identified for the type of event that creates community conflict. The qualifications are: (1) the event must touch peoples' lives; (2) it must affect people differently; and (3) it must be one where action can be taken. According to Coleman, changes in time, differences in economic structure, existing cleavages, and the residuum of past controversy create conditions ripe for conflict. Here emotional, psychological issues combine with practical issues to create strife. Community conflict and its divisive as well as socially redeeming aspects will assuredly be a consideration in many environmental disputes.

Conflict settlement among ethnic groups presents another curiosity for the mediator. In some cases, it appears that conflict among ethnic groups is initiated, fought out, and settled without public disclosure. Or it could be that the ethnic group exerts an authoritarian or totalitarian force on its members, suppressing conflict partially or totally.

Much research has been undertaken in conflict settlement among and within cohesive social and ethnic groups (see, e.g., Spindler and Spindler, 1971). However, an examination of research in this area would suggest that intensive study is not productive for the environmental mediator. Special application of the research to environmental conflict would occur when an ethnic group is a major party to the conflict, as in Indian claims to native lands since occupied by whites. In such a case, thorough background study of the group's life and social conventions is necessary to determine if internal division exists, how the issues relate to the group's social and psychological needs, and the impacts of conflict and settlement on the lives of group members.

Nations experience internal conflict both economically and socially as development occurs. If two or more parties are trying to occupy a limited field (geographic or otherwise) during economic conflict, as Boulding (1962: 190) suggests, conditions are ripe for all sorts of economic/environment confrontations. Since the middle class is often nonexistent in developing nations, social conflict occurs between the Western intelligentsia (leaders of the development effort) and the rich and poor pluralities (Coser, 1967: 194). Such divisions between social classes and the pro-economy and pro-environment factions are instructive in comparison to the environmental movement in the United States.

International conflict also carries implications for the environmental mediator. Law of the sea issues involve both international relations and use of the environment. Donald Straus (1973: 6) of the American Arbitration Association states that "there is a good deal of ferment and new development in the field of international commercial arbitration." This development, he further states, has "relevance to environmental disputes, since so many of the environmental problems arise as a result of international business organizations of one kind or another." Bilder (1973; 1976) has produced two excellent papers on international environmental disputes.

It is beyond the scope of this book to deal at length with conflict settlement (1) in communities, (2) among ethnic groups, and (3) within and between nations. Each of the three topics takes in a substantial literature and theory with indirect relevance to mediation of environmental disputes. The topics are displayed here to acquaint the prospective mediator with their presence. Citations given in this text will introduce the mediator to each topic if such introduction is required by circumstances of a particular dispute.

In summary, conflicts of various scales (from local to regional to national to international) are instructive to the professional considering intervention in any type of dispute. By viewing other disputes, one may develop a perspective on the many aspects of the conflict situation.

- The mediator as integrator.

Regardless of the type of conflict he enters, the mediator is above all an *integrator*. He must unite the parties and issues and facilitate a settlement. To perform integration, the mediator: (1) helps parties identify and confront issues; (2) provides favorable conditions and circumstances for confronting these issues; (3) removes blocks and distortions; (4) establishes norms for rational interactions; (5) identifies solutions; (6) drafts a workable agreement; and (7) helps make the agreement attractive to constituents of negotiators. Deutsch (1973: 382-385) derives the seven functions listed above from readings in industrial negotiations, community disputes, marital therapy, human relations intergroup conflicts, and international conciliations. As previously stated, the carry-over to environmental mediation is a reasonable and realistic one.

As an integrator, the mediator attempts to make the union of two disagreeing parties a *voluntary* union. Coercion, or enforced restraint, is neither desirable nor possible here. Integration, by contrast, means that parties come together voluntarily. The mediator facilitates this integration by providing, along with the functions described by Deutsch the necessary aspect of *conflict regulation*. The blocks and distortions that Deutsch mentioned are termed irrationalities and nonrationalities by Dahrendorf (1959: 228-229). He believes that reduction of irrationalities and removal of nonrationalities are important functions of the mediator.

- The role of compromise.

All of the social and psychological decisions a mediator must make are directed toward *compromise*. Compromise is desirable in many cases when conflicts demand settlements. The desirability of compromise is stressed in much of the literature (e.g., Community Crisis Intervention Project, 1972; Alinsky, quoted in Nicolau and Cormick, 1972: 103, Coser, 1967: 263). Even untrained persons can reasonably forecast the dissatisfaction and frustration which occurs if the party with power is continually and totally gratified by settlement while the "out" group is constantly left out. For whether it is overt knowledge or not, *compromise means change*. By merely agreeing to bargain, both parties are advocating change. Those in power—the "in" group—realize that public opinion and/or threats to environmental health are often overriding issues in a particular case and that the status quo cannot be maintained. Those challenging the "in" group are often vocal advocates of change. It follows that compromise with change is often a psychological need if realistic negotiation is to begin, continue, and end with an effective settlement.

One might argue that mediation should be a search for truth on the part of the mediator and the concerned parties. This concept is a difficult one which, on the surface, has no place in realistic bargaining. Lord and Warner (1973: 107) have noted that "broad general objectives (perhaps better called social goals) such as economic growth, environmental quality, and equity are not useful (in natural resource decisionmaking), as experience has shown." Truth might be included here as an even broader, philosophical goal which is desirable but very subjective and seldom attained in the majority view. The most important factors in settlement are practical ones—what the parties desire, what they may realistically achieve, and which compromise changes the situation and resolves it to the general satisfaction of both parties. No one is ever totally satisfied; the mediator must assure optimum satisfaction for all concerned in light of the realities of the situation.

One might also argue that either choice A (as proposed by development side A) or choice B (as proposed by preservationist side B) may be optimum as a settlement, rather than a lukewarm compromise C. If such is the case, three important questions must be considered. First, who is to decide which solution is optimal? A judge may decide which choice has greater legal support if the case goes to court. A regulator may decide if rule interpretation is involved. And if the political process is well-defined and working within the mediation process, the settlement may be more politically acceptable and, in that sense, optimal.

The second question follows: How are the parties to be satisfied emotionally if either A or B is chosen? The compromise satisfies partial desires of both parties, and may accommodate their most realistic expectations. Some emotional satisfaction is better than none, and could avert a conflict of great magnitude.

The third question concerns time: Is not a speedy settlement ending in a semi-permanent compromise preferable to a prolonged stalemate in which A or B may be chosen or no choice made at all, especially in environmental conflicts? What about the various traumas which may accompany continuation of an environmental dilemma? Solutions are needed and they are needed as quickly as possible.

The three questions and their answers argue for compromise in nearly every conflict situation. But there are cases, real and hypothetical, in which a compromise on the major issue may not be desirable. For instance, if a public utility proposes construction of a 1000 megawatt nuclear power plant and environmental groups oppose construction of any nuclear power plant in the area, a 500 megawatt plant would hardly be a realistic and acceptable compromise.

Figure 5 (drawn from various sources) illustrates the potential benefits of compromise. The vertical scale may be labeled benefit/cost ratio or the public welfare, i.e., some measure of the public good to be derived from a settlement at various points between opposing positions A and B, shown on the horizontal scale. It is difficult to speculate on actual, existing benefits to be derived in any conflict settlement between points A and B, so this hypothesis may be illustrated by an arbitrary, fairly constant line (2). Liberal politicians and advocates of compromise and social change might opt for hypothesis (1), where any compromise position yields relatively greater benefits than does hypothesis (2). Critics of the constant search for compromise might argue hypothesis (3)—that in many cases compromise does harm to the public welfare socially, economically, and environmentally. Proponents of (3) would say that either the 1000 megawatt nuclear power plant should be constructed or no plant at all. Construction of the 500 megawatt "compromise" plant, they might argue, is an absurd alternative since it disbenefits society relative to position A or B.

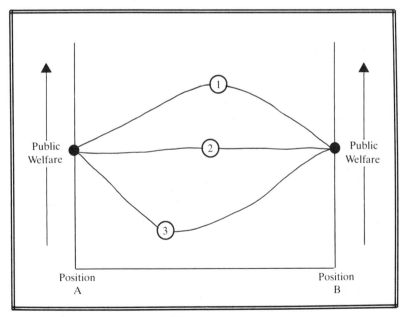

Fig. 5. **Potential benefits of compromise. Hypotheses 1, 2, and 3, as discussed in the text, are illustrated.**

Obviously, settlements are composed of more than either construction or no construction of a nuclear power plant. Side issues, such as disposal of cooling waters, effluent charges, and radioactive waste disposal may be important to the conflict, and side payments or additional mitigation of hazards may make compromise reasonable and acceptable. Energy conservation and enlargement of other plants in the power grid may also be studied. But proponents of hypothesis (3) have a valid point: a pure compromise on the primary issue may not always provide for the optimum public good.

Consideration of hypothesis (3) thrusts other responsibilities upon the mediator. If it is apparent that compromise is undesirable, the mediator can urge an interested third party to promote this view, or bring in an expert to convince the parties of the disadvantages of compromise. Though the mediator may be eliminating the need for his services by pursuing this strategy, he is facilitating communication between parties and helping them look to long-term, broader solutions to the problems. Further, it is the responsibility of the mediator to educate the parties at the outset about: (1) what mediation involves; (2) what mediation requires; and (3) what parties can reasonably expect to achieve (see discussion in Cormick and Patton, 1977). Since mediation does involve compromise, cases in which compromise is not productive must be handled differently by the mediator from potential compromise situations. The potential benefits or disbenefits of compromise (Fig. 5) should be discussed with the parties, and if appropriate, the mediator should either encourage abandonment of the dispute for the time being or a refocussing of issues to make for a potential settlement.

As to the compromise settlement itself, it is difficult to predict settlement potential and even more difficult to predict the short-term and long-term effects of an accommodation. A trained environmental mediator is best suited to aid in both predictions.

In sum, conflict has some positive attributes, but continued conflict produces an imbalance and irregularity which society cannot tolerate. The presence of conflict is healthy; eventual settlement is prerequisite to maintenance of health. It has already been stated that expeditious solutions are needed. Mediation is a useful procedure for fulfilling this need with respect to environmental conflicts.

V.
Mediators and Mediation of Environmental Disputes

The preceding four chapters have provided a conceptual framework for environmental mediation. The components of the framework are: (1) the many dimensions of environmental conflict; (2) the issues and parties to environmental conflict; (3) existing procedures and arrangements that are considered important to the mediation effort or have potential mediatory aspects; and (4) the mediation function, its established uses, and its social and psychological aspects. This chapter discusses the application of mediation processes to environmental disputes.

ENVIRONMENTAL MEDIATION—BACKGROUND AND EXISTING EFFORTS

Mediation of environmental disputes has received attention since 1969 from a small but active group of advocates. Max Ways (1971: 256-257) was one of the first to speak about the need in the United States for tens of thousands of "integrators" to deal with environmental problems. These persons would deal with environmental knowledge both from natural and from social sciences to help resolve questions of human value, law, and purpose that lie beyond the sciences. Ways stated that "the universities that trained us how to take the world apart will now have to train men who will take the lead in putting it together again."

Judge Miles Lord, in his opinion written for *U.S. v. Reserve Mining* (1974b), speaks eloquently of the balancing required in environmental lawsuits. This innovative and controversial jurist stated that "any environmental litigation must involve a balancing of economic dislocation with the environmental benefits." Lord won acclaim for his emphasis on this balancing principle both in and out of court. The appeals court modified and remanded his decision, but noted his

> innovative techniques in trying this case by bringing into court some of the world's leading scientists, physicians, and other experts in seeking resolution of the controversy before him (*Reserve Mining v. U.S.*, 1974).

Immediately prior to its commendation of Lord's work, the appeals court spoke directly to the use of mediation in this case. Judge Bright wrote

> At oral argument counsel for all parties indicated that the controversy ought now to be settled. Counsel for Reserve suggested a Master or Referee ought to be appointed who could 'in some way establish some mechanism that could focus on whether or not there is a reasonable basis for resolution of this controversy.' Counsel for the United States indicated amenability to settlement, stating 'I think this case ultimately ought to be settled.' Counsel for the State of Minnesota at argument advised the court that Judge Lord during trial contemplated keeping Reserve in operation conditioned upon future settlement.

Bright went on to say

> We think settlement of this kind of case represents a necessary and desirable goal, and the matter should be pursued in the district court. One possible approach is the use of *mediation techniques* in resolving disputes on technical matters by using experts from business and sci-

ence who can assist the parties in reaching a settlement or can advise the district court on technical matters in his consideration of Reserve's plan (emphasis added).

The second quotation above might be taken to mean that the Master or Referee would be confined to the role of an officer of the court—to hear, investigate, report, and perhaps settle by judgment a legal matter, as assigned by the court. The Master's or Referee's service would traditionally be confined to findings of fact. But the third quotation above and the context in which both quotations appear suggests that the court had in mind more than findings of fact. The direct mention of "mediation techniques," the reference to resolution of disputes on "technical matters by using experts from business and science," and the commendation of Lord's "innovative techniques" all suggest, in the context of the opinion, that the court was proposing something new, different, and beyond the bounds of the traditional Master or Referee. One immediately thinks of the "science court" discussed in Chapter One, and agreement by opposing parties on findings of fact with the assistance of a third party.

Charles H.W. Foster (1969; also see descriptive footnote 1975a) was perhaps the first to speak directly of "environmental conciliation." His use of conciliation described resolution of the matter in dispute, as opposed to third party intervention on Simkin's most passive level (Fig. 3, Chapter 4).

Foster described in detail the current and historical background for mediation services, but noted that "application of professional conciliation practices to environmental and conservation issues has been discussed but never formally attempted." He believed that private mediation should be employed initially, with resort to a fact-finding board if resolution was not forthcoming. Concerning practical apsects, Foster stated that environmental mediators could be found; a suitable organizational structure existed for pilot efforts; and, on balance, the prognosis was promising for environmental conciliation. Moreover, he based his prognosis on talks with experienced mediators of labor and community disputes. Foster demonstrated the modest cost, speedy resolution, and innovative but enormously productive potential of environmental conciliation.

The pioneering ideas of Foster and others were developed further by Gerald Cormick and Jane McCarthy of the Community Crisis Intervention Center (CCIC), Washington University, St. Louis, Missouri. Cormick and McCarthy discussed environmental mediation in 1973, during McCarthy's term on the staff of the environment division of the Ford Foundation in New York and Cormick's term with CCIC. Cormick eventually presented a proposal to the Ford and Rockefeller Foundations requesting funds for one or two skilled mediators, a small research staff, and a developmental conference on the subject (Cormick, 1973). In the proposal Cormick cited several instances in which lengthy talks with environmentalists, lawyers (representing industry, environmental groups, and public agencies), industry and corporate spokesmen, government agency staff, and political decisionmakers indicated a keen interest in mediation of environmental conflict and a belief that the process was feasible (see Appendix).

Cormick subsequently presented a paper on environmental mediation at Environment '74 International Symposium III in Spokane, Washington (Cormick, 1974). In the meantime, he and Jane McCarthy became involved in actual mediation of an environmental dispute concerning flood control and recreation on the Snoqualmie River in Washington. Chapter 6 presents a detailed analysis of this dispute.

The Snoqualmie effort received national exposure in *The Environment Action Bulletin* (1975), *Conflict* newsletter (McCarthy, 1974), and *The Professional Geographer* (Mernitz, 1975). On local scales, articles in Seattle, Washington newspapers, *The Milwaukee Journal* (Mernitz, 1976) and *The Rocky Mountain News* (Moya, 1977) in Denver have informed readers about environmental mediation and its successful application in the Snoqualmie dispute. (Cormick and his staff have since relocated in the Office of Environmental Mediation in the Institute for Environmental Studies, University of Washington, Seattle).

Several steps, both tentative and assertive, have been taken concerning further, practical application of environmental mediation theory. One citizen's group in Wisconsin suggested in 1975 that (former) Governor Patrick Lucey use mediation techniques for settlement of an environmental dispute in that state. The conflict was over flood control and recreation in the Kickapoo River valley in southwest Wisconsin. Many issues in the Kickapoo situation were similar to those of the Snoqualmie, and application of mediation techniques appeared feasible. One source (Adams, 1975) suggested that the sensitive political and budgetary status of the case prevented mediation from becoming a realistic alternative to litigation or continuing conflict.

Cormick's work has also attracted the attention of Colorado politicians, environmental groups, and water users in general. The Foothills water treatment plant, proposed for construction southwest of Denver, has generated much controversy. In mid-1977, Congresswoman Pat Schroeder of Colorado suggested that Cormick's office be called in to mediate disagreements over sources of future water supply for the plant. In 1978 and early 1979, Colorado Congressman Tim Wirth helped to organize meetings, with the U.S. Army Corps of Engineers as technical "mediator," which led to an eventual out-of-court settlement involving the Denver Water Board, the Corps, the Water Users Alliance, EPA, and the U.S. Department of the Interior.

Due primarily to the efforts of Charles Foster, environmental mediation has been considered for implementation in Massachusetts. Foster was formerly Secretary of the Massachusetts Executive Office of Environmental Affairs. His office attempted to draft and file legislation (see Appendix) pertaining to environmental mediation during the 1974 session (Foster, 1975a). Foster felt that the pressures of an election year were primarily responsible for failure to submit the legislation. In the initial, draft bill, total annual expenses were estimated at $50,000; $25,000 for a staff director and overhead expenses, and $25,000 for mediation expenses that could not be borne by principals to the dispute.

Later word from Foster (1975b) indicated that program legislation was again not introduced during the 1975 session. Further details of the proposed act were available, however.

A decision was made to seek state funds to finance the mediation service, subject to possible reimbursement by the parties on a negotiated, proportional basis. Expenses by this time were estimated at $75,000 yearly and would come from a special Environmental Fund rather than from state General Fund sources. Mediators would be contract public employees, and therefore not subject to real or alleged conflict of interest.

Foster's successor (Murphy, 1976) noted still later that there had been no further attempts to file the mediation legislation in the new administration. A few modifications had been made in the statutory language, however; an informational copy is included in the Appendix.

The Environmental Balance Association of Minnesota, Inc. (EBA) has promoted environmental mediation in that state (Karlstrand, 1976). EBA, an organization of labor and industry groups advocating a balance between a healthy economy and a quality environment, mediated a dispute over construction of a barley malting plant in Moorhead, Minnesota. The effort resulted in withdrawal of a lawsuit by the petitioner on May 14, 1976 (see Appendix).

A news article concerning mediation in Minnesota (Karlstrand, 1976) mentions the continuing progress of Cormick and McCarthy. Their Office of Environmental Mediation (OEM) at the University of Washington was awarded $125,000 in 1975 by the Ford and Rockefeller Foundations to resolve environmental disputes involving river basin development, strip mining, and timber harvesting in the Pacific Northwest and British Columbia. The OEM has since successfully mediated the Seattle I-90 freeway dispute in which citizen groups, local administrators, and the State Highway Commission agreed upon a transportation plan that would hold suburban sprawl in check. What began as a promising idea is being tested and proved by OEM and others.

And many others are exploring various approaches and techniques in response to environmental conflicts. Some of their processes and findings were discussed in an environmental mediation symposium sponsored by the American Association for the Advancement of Science at its Annual Meeting in

Denver, Colorado, during February, 1977. Peter Clark of the Center for Energy Policy in Boston described his organization's work to facilitate multi-party processes in development of energy policy in the northeast United States. Laura Lake (1977) of the University of California, Los Angeles, discussed her use of mediation and conflict avoidance techniques concerning power plant options for California. Paul Wehr (1976) of the University of Colorado, Boulder, talked of his "environmental conciliation" project, involving local interest groups and a large ski area development proposed for the Colorado Rockies. And Donald Straus (1977) of the Research Institute of the American Arbitration Association in New York City presented a paper on "data mediation"—resolving conflicts among diverse groups over acceptable and reliable data regarding broad issues, such as coastal zone management. Each participant, and the many discussants who attended the symposium reinforced the validity of, and national interest in, mediation of environmental, energy, and economic trade-offs.

Another important conference on environmental conflict resolution was held during January, 1978 at Reston, Virginia. Co-sponsors of the conference were RESOLVE, Center for Environmental Conflict Resolution; the Aspen Institute for Humanistic Studies; and the Sierra Club Foundation. The topic was "Environmental Mediation: An Effective Alternative?" Much worthwhile discussion resulted, and an excellent summary report was produced by RESOLVE (1978).

The discussants at the Reston conference exemplified the growing numbers of environmental intervenors. Gerald Cormick was there, telling of his work on the Snoqualmie and Interstate-90 disputes. Susan Carpenter of ROMCOE-Center for Environmental Problem Solving, Denver, spoke of ROMCOE's work in Colorado, emphasizing their notions of "conflict anticipation" and "conflict assessment." Lawrence Moss described the bi-lateral task force negotiations of the National Coal Policy Project. And Malcolm Rivkin of Rivkin Associates added his perspective, that of a private consultant, hired by a developer to negotiate with an opposing local citizens' group over construction of a large shopping mall.

Later in 1978, another private consultant, Clark-Mc-Glennon Associates (Peter Clark), teamed with the American Arbitration Association (Don Straus) and the Resources and Land Investigation (RALI) Program, U.S. Department of Interior, to prepare a set of guidelines to identify, manage and resolve environmental disputes. Application of these guidelines to actual dispute cases has followed.

In addition to the above efforts, many others are working in environmental conflict resolution. The literature is growing. The topic and its techniques are definitely receiving nationwide attention.

RESOLVE wishes to act as a national clearinghouse to (1) organize conflict resolution services, (2) collect and disseminate information, (3) sponsor research, (4) review existing institutions and formulate recommendations for improvements, and (5) assist in developing regional conflict resolution centers and providing mediator referral services. Funding for a multi-year effort has been provided from private foundations.

Related to existing efforts at environmental mediation are the topics of (1) what institution will mediate? and (2) which individuals will be mediators? While it is not the purpose of this handbook to treat these topics in detail, a few comments might prove useful.

First, regarding institutions, it would appear that every level of government—from federal to regional to state to local—would have obvious advantages and disadvantages as the institutional location for an established, public-funded mediation service. Each level of government has been considered at one time or another in the past decade, with some trial attempts and some partial successes (e.g., see RESOLVE, 1978: 23-25, Busterud, 1979: 5,8).

Presently, institutional mediation services have achieved greatest success at universities and as non-profit, charitable organizations. Cormick's Office of Environmental Mediation at the University of Washington, Seattle, is a well-established example of the former, while RESOLVE is a newly-established example of the latter. Both are funded by private foundations, helping to assure impartiality.

Second, regarding individuals, training in many disciplines would seem most desirable, since environmental mediation often involves interdisciplinary analysis. Those persons in the United States now working in or proposing to practice environmental mediation are of diverse educational backgrounds, including law, labor and international dispute settlement, engineering, psychology, biology/ecology, political science, and geography/ environmental studies. Personal interest and involvement are also prerequisites for an effective mediator. They will lead to the greatest teacher: experience. One cannot personally know how people interact in an environmental bargaining situation until the event actually occurs and is witnessed.

EXAMPLES OF MEDIATION TECHNIQUES

A number of third-party techniques have been used to deal with environmental disputes throughout the United States. Many of these, depending upon one's point of view, can be loosely termed "mediation." A few will be briefly surveyed here to illustrate practical applications of environmental mediation theory.

Shuttle diplomacy

The efforts of Charles Warren, former Chairman of the President's Council on Environmental Quality, concerned mediation of a dispute between California and Nevada to control pollution in Lake Tahoe (Fogarty, 1978). The agreement centered on membership and jurisdiction of the bi-state Tahoe Regional Planning Agency (TRPA). Warren helped the states to reach the initial agreement by practicing a Kissinger-style shuttle diplomacy (between Sacramento hotel rooms instead of Middle Eastern countries, in this case). He carried messages, proposals, and counter-proposals back and forth, and noted that the negotiations were "a lot of work and took a lot of patience." As in many resource disputes, the final solution appeared rather simple but was the result of considerable negotiation. Warren was invited by the governors of California and Nevada to serve as mediator, aiding his credibility and sanction.

However, the agreement eventually proved weak when Nevada legislators did not approve the mediated settlement. It now appears federal action will be taken to regulate growth in the Tahoe Basin.

Non-directive consensus-building

Third party facilitators have used different techniques in Colorado. In one instance, RESOLVE used a non-directive approach to attempt to build consensus among diverse parties over proposed wilderness areas in Colorado. The RESOLVE effort was accepted by (and partially funded by) the U.S. Forest Service as part of the citizen comment period for the RARE II program in Colorado. (RARE II is the second phase of a national *R*oadless *A*rea *R*eview and *E*valuation.)

RESOLVE's non-directive approach involved, first, a recognition that the initial task of the facilitators was to educate the parties about the consensus process itself (RESOLVE, 1979: III-2). Second, the facilitators recognized that the parties would go through several stages before they developed a group identity and could assume responsibility for decisionmaking. RESOLVE chose not to place itself in a "suggestive" mode, in which it would suggest a process and direct its use if adopted. Instead, group "ownership" of the process was stressed.

Third, in evaluating their approach, RESOLVE noted that several barriers blocked unanimous consensus on more than a few areas. Among the major barriers were a) a lack of time (about 4 1/2 months), b) a broad set of disputes over many separate geographic areas (over 230), and c) a large number of diffuse interests and participants (at least 50).

Information sharing and conciliation

ROMCOE has used techniques of information sharing and conciliation to manage environmental conflict (Carpenter and Kennedy, 1977: 21-22). Their staff worked with citizens and interest groups in Mesa County, Colorado, to address the conversion of agricultural land to other uses in this, one of the outstanding fruit and vegetable-producing regions of the state. By organizing a workshop, proposing important and relevant discussion questions, and promoting the sharing of information, ROMCOE was able to help Mesa County citizens recognize the potential for conflict, anticipate its effects, and begin efforts to manage it. The workshop set the stage for continued information sharing in the county.

Bi-lateral task force negotiations

On a larger scale, the National Coal Policy Project has used a bi-lateral task force negotiations process to initiate a series of field trips and talks involving environmentalists and coal producing and consuming industries. Two influential persons, one from each side, appear to be the prime movers behind the discussions. Consensus has been reached on a number of important points of coal policy, and other technical agreements include recommendations for a) areas of the nation in which to concentrate coal mining, b) air pollution control, and c) electricity pricing. The agreements have been proposed for implementation to the Congress, EPA, and other federal and state agencies (RESOLVE, 1978: 44-46).

Dialectical scanning

A general technique used in the planning profession is also employed by environmental mediators. Dialectical scanning is a long name for a simple, common-sense notion: if two or more parties are apparently in conflict over particular issues, sit them down with a mediator, focus on the conflicting issues, and find out if and why conflict exists. Often, there are conflicts due to (1) factual misunderstandings, (2) differences about cause/effect relationships regarding impacts, or (3) differences in values (Hudson, Wachs, and Schafer, 1974). The first two can be resolved by consistent information-sharing; the third, unfortunately, often blocks all resolution efforts (see discussion of values in Chapter Two).

Scoping

The Council on Environmental Quality issued new regulations for implementing the National Environmental Policy Act on

November 29, 1978. At least one provision in the new regulations provides a mechanism for resolving conflicts at an early stage. This is the scoping process. The regulations state:

> *There shall be an early and open process for determining the scope of issues to be addressed and for identifying the significant issues related to a proposed action. This process shall be termed scoping.* (43 Fed. Reg. 55978.)

The scoping process, according to the guidelines (*Current Developments,* Vol. 10, No. 8), will follow the determination that an environmental impact statement will be required. All affected federal, state, and local agencies, the grantee, and other interested parties must be invited to attend the scoping sessions.

At the time of this writing (June 1979), the U.S. Forest Service is undertaking a scoping effort in connection with the Mt. Emmons Project, a proposed molybdenum mine, mill, and tailings complex near Crested Butte, Colorado. The project is sponsored by AMAX, Inc.; the Forest Service is the federal lead agency.

While the scoping process has not yet been used enough by federal agencies to be able to assess its effectiveness, it has been employed in Massachusetts. The Massachusetts Environmental Policy Act has a scoping provision which has made possible a successful forum for negotiation among concerned parties. Raymond Ghelardi, Associate Planner with the Executive Office of Environmental Affairs in Boston, has reported on numerous applications of scoping which have resulted in project plans being modified during the informal sessions, to the satisfaction of all concerned. (*Environmental Consensus,* Vol. 2, No. 1; Vol. 2, No. 2.)

THE NEGOTIATED AGREEMENT

After a particular environmental conflict is recognized, the negotiating parties assembled, and the mediator's services retained, work proceeds toward one end: the negotiated agreement. By this time the parties have agreed to negotiate in good faith toward one compromise solution, and that solution must take written form. Following are comments, suggestions, and specific examples of negotiated agreements in environmental disputes.

Parties to the negotiated agreement are usually a developer or developers, various environmental or citizen groups and one or more agencies or governments at local, state, regional, or federal levels responsible for overseeing implementation of the agreement. If no legal document has been filed officially recognizing the dispute, the dispute may "exist" only in the media and in the minds of the conflicting parties. The agreement and the form it takes could in this circumstance be more politically than legally binding, according to Cormick (1977). Settlement may be in the form of a memorandum establishing certain conditions which all parties sign with the understanding that they will enforce the conditions stated therein by mutual consent. Usual practice is to form an implementation committee composed of representatives of the negotiating groups.

If a lawsuit has been filed challenging a proposed development, the negotiated agreement can take a technical, legal form in the record of court proceedings. It is not uncommon for plaintiffs and defendants to agree, prior to the termination of a lawsuit in court, to dismiss the suit on certain conditions. The settlement in this case may take the form of a stipulation, order for dismissal with prejudice, and stipulation for dismissal (three separate documents) filed in the court of record and signed by the presiding judge. The documents consequently become part of the record of litigation when the suit is withdrawn.

Dismissed "with prejudice" means that the same litigation cannot be reopened unless circumstances change. It is the understanding of one mediator (Fradin, 1977) that "if the stipulation is not adhered to by one party or the other, then the courts can be appealed to for enforcement on the basis of the stipulation."

Another type of settlement may result if, under statute, a state or federal agency has the authority to conduct hearings and order remedial action upon petition by an interested party. Such an out-of-court settlement may result in findings of fact, conclusions of law, and a consent order pertaining to the dispute.

The types of documents described above have been used in specific circumstances (examples are included in Appendix). The Snoqualmie, Washington dispute was settled using a memorandum-type agreement, as was the Seattle I-90 controversy. The Colorado Land Use Commission (1977) has also used a memorandum-type agreement to compromise over land development issues, specifically regarding withdrawal of its regulatory authority halting development of a proposed subdivision. The Moorhead, Minnesota malt plant dispute resulted in the legal stipulations described above. The matter of a proposed solid waste disposal site in northwest Wisconsin was settled using the findings of fact, consent order, and conclusions of law described above. All of these (and perhaps other innovations) might be used to document the mediated settlement.

VI.
Environmental Conflict Case Studies

A discussion of the potential application of mediation to environmental disputes must necessarily consider several case studies of conflict. The case studies include various stages and sizes of conflicts; furthermore, different kinds of disputants, impacts, and sectors of the environment will be examined. A consideration of such an array of case studies can be expected to lead to preliminary conclusions regarding the mediability of disputes.

CASE STUDIES IN GENERAL

Preliminary remarks will be addressed to potential classification schemes and analysis methods for environmental disputes; these will be reviewed after investigation of actual experiences.

Bilder (1976: 7), in his excellent analysis of international environmental disputes, suggests several ways in which such disputes may be classified. Adaptations of his categories are useful in distinguishing among environmental disputes on the basis of the following criteria:

(1) the central theme of the dispute: facts and assessments of these facts; existing and new rules and their interpretations and application;

(2) the relation of the dispute to conduct which has en-
    vironmental consequences, and/or to jurisdiction
    over environmentally relevant conduct;
(3) the parties to the dispute;
(4) the geographical scope of the dispute;
(5) the sector of the environment primarily affected;
(6) the nature of the polluting agent and its source;
(7) the character of conduct giving rise to the dispute:
    intentional or not, one time or continuing, and so
    forth;
(8) the scope of potential impact: local or widespread,
    direct or subtle; and
(9) the kind of remedy sought: monetary damages, in-
    junctions, or other types; and against whom: individ-
    ual, corporation, or the government.

Bilder states that, in general, international environmental
disputes have been approached on the basis of the environmental sector primarily affected (5 above). He used the environmental sector classification in his discussions, but mentions its obvious limitations.

Similarly, those environmental dispute case studies analyzed in this chapter (all occurring within the United States or
principally involving this nation) will be categorized by the
environmental sector primarily affected. Preliminary analysis
of the case studies suggests that the environmental sector classification will be useful but not completely satisfactory.

To be explicit, the major problem with this classification
is that no environmental dispute is limited solely to one sector
of the environment. Mineral extraction and processing may
create air and water pollution, in addition to having social,
economic, and political impacts. Natural and human systems
are invariably affected, thus involving all sectors of the environment. The environmental sector classification has difficulty
for other minor reasons, but unfortunately the other classification types have similar problems or are too general.

A prospective mediator might also consider subclassifications which may be of potential use. Using the subclasses,
he might further categorize disputes by principal environmen-

tal sectors. For example, the mediator might determine whether a compromise did occur, or if a compromise alternative existed. He might determine if there were existing, ancillary, negotiable factors that were not part of the initial dispute. He might classify disputes chronologically, by evolutionary stage of conflict. Finally, he might analyze the geographical scope, parties involved, and other factors mentioned by Bilder.

It is obvious from this discussion that classification promotes analysis, and vice versa. Virtually all of Bilder's nine criteria (in addition to the subclassifications just mentioned above and alluded to in preceding chapters) will furnish some insight into a particular case study. It remains to determine how classifications may be used to differentiate mediable disputes from those that are not mediable.

CASE STUDIES IN PARTICULAR

The object of this chapter is to survey past environmental disputes. A summary and analysis will be presented, with synthesis to follow in concluding chapters. In most cases a reference will be given for further reading. In several instances, however, the information is derived from correspondences, interviews, news clips, or personal evaluation and impression. References will be omitted in these instances.

Each case study will be presented in the following sequence: (1) general comments including comparisons with other cases; (2) general background discussion with dates, places, names, and (in some cases) maps or diagrams; (3) detailed comparison and analysis; and (4) discussions of the mediable aspects of each dispute.

Any classification scheme has its limitations, and the limitations of the scheme used here will become more apparent as the case studies are analyzed. For purposes of this chapter, environmental conflicts will be classified under the following headings:

water resources - case studies primarily involving surface or subsurface water resources;

land resources - case studies primarily involving surface or subsurface soil, rocks and minerals, plants and animals (excluding man);

air resources - case studies primarily involving the earth's atmosphere in micro- or macro-scale;

human resources - case studies primarily involving the special impacts of developments on humans, with consideration of issues such as aesthetics and quality of life.

The reader should note that the case studies presented here will be analyzed at a certain "moment in time"—i.e., the original analysis was performed during January-May, 1976, and the description and analysis of each case study will be current for that period. The original analysis is retained in order that the reader may be exposed to several disputes at varying stages of conflict. Selected disputes have been updated for the sake of completeness.

By monitoring the field of environmental disputes, one begins to understand that some conflicts are never completely resolved; they are dormant for a time, only to resurface at a later date. Moreover, new and unrelated cases of conflict, though unique in character, often involve elements associated with disputes in the past.

Water Resources

RESERVE MINING COMPANY (MINNESOTA)

Setting

Geographic Scale. The Reserve dispute is particularly instructive because it combines the issues of economy, employment, and environment in a classic fashion. Reserve, mentioned previously, has received national attention. The basic issue is alleged pollution of Lake Superior, an international lake, by Reserve Mining Company, Silver Bay, as a result of the processing of taconite ore and discharge of effluent containing asbestos-like waste particles into the lake (see Fig. 6).

Parties. Air pollution from the processing has been previously raised as an issue, accepted as valid by Reserve, and

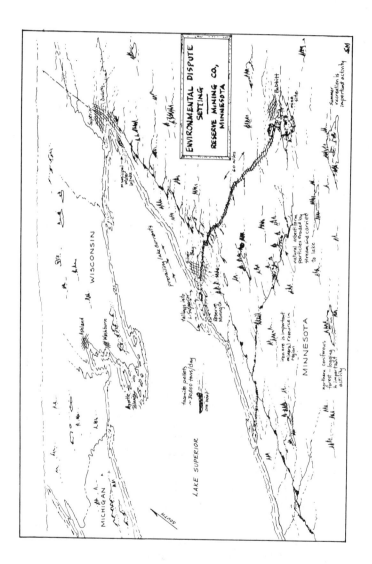

Fig. 6. Map-picture depicting the environmental dispute setting for the Reserve Mining Company dispute, Minnesota.

dealt with effectively. The presence (alleged to be cancer-causing) of asbestos-like particles in the drinking water of northern Minnesota residents and the degradation of Lake Superior as a unique water resource in areas contiguous to Canada, Michigan, and Wisconsin are two primary issues advanced by environmentalists. Reserve is alleged to be discharging up to 67,000 tons of taconite tailings into Lake Superior each day and to be earning up to a $60,000 daily profit. Approximately 3,000 people, or 90% of the population of Silver Bay, work for Reserve. Due to the above issues, the State of Minnesota entered into a lawsuit against Reserve. Canada, Michigan and Wisconsin, supportive of Minnesota's stance, were also involved.

Stage of dispute. Reserve has been involved in hearings, conferences, and studies on the impacts of its tailings disposal since 1947. Conflicts over its use of Lake Superior came into focus, however, when the United States began legal proceedings against Reserve in 1972. Since that time the federal government, the state governments of Minnesota, Wisconsin, and Michigan, and various legally recognized intervenors have been active in court proceedings, hearings, and other discussions and meetings with Reserve.

Resolution Efforts

Role of the third party. Out-of-court negotiation was attempted during the period of legal proceedings. Judge Lord tried to bring technical experts together out of court to resolve certain issues. The appeals court noted his efforts at mediation and suggested further use of mediation techniques, using an impartial third party (see Chapter 5). Reserve attempted to negotiate with the State of Minnesota during the trial, and one attorney associated with Reserve who possessed previous arbitration experience was involved. These efforts on the part of various parties resolved little, however.

The political role of Governor Wendell Anderson of Minnesota is worthy of study in the Reserve case. In 1973, Anderson issued a directive prohibiting use of tailings in road work in the state after hearing testimony on potential carcinogenic effects. Later, however, he replaced Minnesota Pollution Control Authority (PCA) Director Grant Merritt, considered a friend to environmentalists, with a less-experienced former Anderson aide and lobbyist. Merritt had resigned under what his advocates described as continuous pressure over the Reserve case. It is interesting to note that Anderson had, as a legislator, once introduced a bill calling for an environmental user fee to be levied against Reserve. Later, as governor, he had urged a delay in the progress of a similar bill.

Anderson played no apparent mediation role in the Reserve case. He stayed out of the limelight but made politically expedient gestures when the situation was right. This example shows that a state's chief executive may have influence at various stages of an environmental conflict. The actions of governors will be examined in other case studies.

Compromise plans. The lack of success for mediation techniques in this conflict can be attributed to Reserve's resistance, because of its ultimate goal of maximum profits. Reserve took a very "hard line" by continuing to operate the plant in spite of massive public protest, to the detriment of the public image of the steel industry. There exists the strong possibility that Reserve was merely trying to exhaust all legal delays (and they have been considerable ones) before finally closing the plant ahead of projected schedule. Reserve had threatened to close soon and observers thought this to be a real possibility. Reserve had nothing to gain and much to lose by negotiating a settlement involving any curtailment of operations during the legal proceedings. To Reserve's ultimate benefit, the scarcity of jobs in northern Minnesota intensified economic and political arguments against closure.

Another political consideration worthy of note is the shift of responsibility as overseer of Reserve's clean-up efforts from the federal government to the State of Minnesota. The Justice Department and the Environmental Protection Agency (EPA) played major roles in the early litigation, but in March of 1975, the EPA announced they were turning the case over to the Minnesota PCA. The political and regulatory arena was thereby drastically narrowed.

Mediability

The Reserve Mining case can be categorized with those unsuitable for mediation. It became excessively complex, lengthy, and expensive. Reserve had nothing to lose by delay. No shared interest in settlement existed. If a shared interest in settlement had existed, and if the political importance of the dispute had been minimized (or used to advantage by Governor Anderson), mediation could have led in the early stages to on-land tailings disposal, for which the Reserve Mining Company is now deliberately preparing.

PCBs IN THE HUDSON RIVER (NEW YORK)

Setting

Geographic scale. The discharge of PCBs (polychlorinated biphenyls) as pollutants into the Hudson River created an interesting controversy in New York State. Like that of Reserve Mining, the Hudson PCB case is a statewide dispute with national impact. The PCB manufacturing process was formerly used throughout the United States; however, many states are now taking a second look. The decision on PCBs in New York will be felt nationwide.

PCBs are stable liquids used mainly as insulating fluids in electrical equipment. Since 1929, PCBs have also been used in such products as paints, plastics, rubber, and inks. The chemicals have been linked to toxic effects in laboratory animals, allegedly causing liver cancer, reproductive system failure, skin diseases, and nervous disorders.

Parties. In 1975, two environmental groups petitioned the Food and Drug Administration (FDA) to have the federal PCB tolerances in food reduced to zero because of alleged toxic effects. The petition tactic had met with earlier success in cases involving DDT, the SST, and lead in gasoline. Petitioners presented a *prima facie* case and requested a review of federal regulations and immediate temporary relief from the alleged injury until a new determination was made by the relevant agency (see Landau and Rheingold, 1971: 215-410).

General Electric Company (GE) is the alleged offending industry in the Hudson PCB case. The case presents an interesting twist because GE offered, in April of 1976, to pay the state at least $2 million to settle the controversy. Under reported terms of the proposed agreement, the payment would not be cited as a penalty, nor would the company be required to make "restoration, reclamation, or other like remedy" because of its discharge. GE also insisted the state sign a "good faith clause" essentially absolving the company from causing direct intentional harm to Hudson River waters and indirect damage to residents of areas including and contiguous to the Hudson drainage basin (Severo, 1976).

Stage of dispute. The actions of New York Conservation Commissioner Ogden Reid and New York Governor Hugh Carey are central to the PCB conflict. Carey and Reid had a strained relationship because of the differences over the PCB case and other matters. Reid came out against acceptance of monetary damages as a suitable compromise. And, although Carey publicly supported Reid's positions on environmental issues, the strength of Carey's support was suspect because of the Governor's obvious need to promote New York's financial health. Reid further inflamed the situation when he noted, in a public statement, the precedent-setting aspects of the case. Reid's press release apparently provoked a public statement from Associated Industries of New York, which expressed its concern for the potential effects of an unfavorable decision: serious economic consequences to its member industries. The Associated Industries statement appeared to accentuate the split.

Resolution Efforts

Evidence of potential compromise is present, however. Reid and his staff had negotiated with GE to reach a settlement, with no success. Reid had previously compromised and agreed to an extension of his zero discharge deadline. The central issue is complete exoneration for GE, which Reid apparently would not accept in light of his concerns for public health and welfare. Reid resigned amidst the PCB issue and other controversies in May, 1976.

Once again the roles of the governor and his subordinates are worthy of study. Reid's frustration with the negotiations and his lack of support from the state's chief executive had caused him to accentuate the conflict. Public statements had been made, revealing only what was common knowledge but nonetheless making positions appear irreconcilable.

An update of this case study to June, 1979, reveals that a settlement between GE and the State of New York was reached in September, 1976. About $7 million was involved — $4 million paid by GE for clean-up and research, and $3 million added by the State.

Commissioner Burley, who replaced Commissioner Reid and served until December, 1978, signed the agreement on behalf of the New York Department of Environmental Conservation. Details on the negotiations are, unfortunately, not available.

Since 1976, an accelerated research effort has been undertaken to identify the effects of PCBs on plant and animal life in the Hudson and to locate "hot spots" where PCBs are concentrated. Additional funding is being sought from EPA, since the initial fund is substantially depleted and a costly dredging program is proposed. A conference on the topic of PCBs in the Hudson River is slated for mid-1979, both to report on research results and to call attention to the need for federal government assistance (Davis, 1979).

Mediability

The dispute was one susceptible to mediation, but only if strained relations could have been repaired by a third party who could also restrain provocative press releases. These repairs apparently were undertaken. Since negotiations had already taken place, parties were designated to a great extent. The Governor and his aides had taken part in previous negotiations and probably aided in the mediation effort.

Further, General Electric had an old and hard-earned public image to maintain. A monetary settlement clearly exonerating GE from any wrongdoing did promote good public relations, and was probably used in advertising copy. The settlement price was small compared to the antagonism of many potential customers in New York and the United States.

Settlement of the Hudson PCB case was undoubtedly viewed with interest by industry and by those concerned with PCBs in the Great Lakes and other waters. GE agreed to stop discharge of PCBs into the Hudson and to assist in the clean-up—a settlement that apparently satisfied the people of New York.

SNOQUALMIE RIVER (WASHINGTON)

Setting

Geographic scale. The dispute, involving flood control and recreation on the Snoqualmie River in Washington, attracted the attention of Gerald Cormick (then of Washington University, St. Louis, Missouri) about 1973. Cormick was subsequently joined in his mediation effort by Jane McCarthy. Figure 7 presents a chronology of events in this first, overt effort to mediate an environmental conflict.

Some discussion of this chronology of events will be informative. The Corps of Engineers had originally proposed dams on both the North and Middle Forks of the Snoqualmie. Various plans were considered by the negotiators before parties agreed on a dam on the North Fork and a strong land use management plan to protect farmlands, forests, and open space in other parts of the basin (Fig. 8). Other recommendations included raising the spillway on the Tolt River Reservoir, minimum lot sizes of 10 acres in various parts of the valley, undeveloped status for parts of the Snohomish River basin, and economic studies of agricultural development in parts of the Snohomish basin.

As to the negotiations themselves, some discussion from a paper by Cormick and Patton (1977: 17) is instructive.

"The environmentalists discovered that the farmers did not wish to sell their land to subdividers and would, in fact, support stringent controls to prevent such development. The residents of the town and surrounding areas

1959   Snoqualmie River basin floods; public outcry by valley residents for federal assistance; problem brought to the attention of Army Corps of Engineers.

1968   after nine years of study, Corps concludes two storage dams should be built on upper reaches of river

1968   second public outcry, led by environmentalists, against Corps proposals

1970   Governor of Washington, after receiving formal Corps report, says "no" to dam because of adverse environmental impact; Governor orders a public review cycle to explore non-structural alternative flood control measures; a series of hearings are held, and valley residents and environmentalists emerge as distinct opponents in the dispute, with legal action threatened by each side

1973   Governor again says "no" to dam on same grounds as in 1970, but notes that he continues to be concerned about the flooding problem

1973   (Fall) Community Crisis Intervention Center (CCIC) makes initial inquiries to determine whether the Snoqualmie dispute would lend itself to mediation; Cormick offers services to Governor after determining suitability of the dispute for mediation; notice of acceptance of mediator kept from public until mediator could become acquainted with disputants to establish an atmosphere of trust; during the next five months, mediators carry on an informal intervention, with no negotiations

1974   (May) formal mediation effort announced by Governor in press release; release stressed that funds for the mediation effort were provided by the Ford and Rockefeller Foundations, showing the financial independence of the mediation team

1974   (May-August) a series of meetings are held by the mediators with ten "core group" representatives from different parties to the dispute, each representing himself only but responsible for delivering his constituents

1974   (late August) mediation effort appears to reach stalemate, because of inability of environmental group to formulate a common position in response to the position of those primarily interested in flood control

1974   (September) deadlock finally breaks; tentative agreement begins to take shape

1974   (December) "after two months of painstaking efforts to formulate specific provisions and final language, all the participants in the mediation effort signed a set of joint recommendations to be forwarded to the Governor"; Governor indicates he, along with all negotiating groups, "thoroughly endorse[s]" the recommendations (Cormick and McCarthy, 1974: 5-6)

Fig. 7.   A chronology of events in the Snoqualmie River (Washington) dispute.

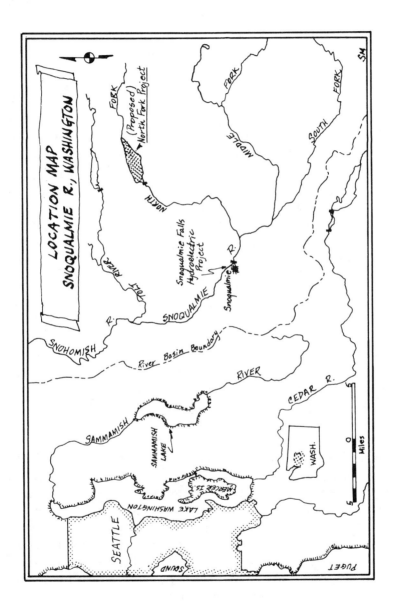

Fig. 8

began to listen to and understand the development concerns of environmentalists and recognized that uncontrolled development would make the valley less desirable to them as well. The environmentalists discovered that sprawl was occurring legally and illegally despite the flooding, and that continued flooding was not, in itself, an adequate tool for growth control. The environmentalists also began to perceive that any 'win' predicated only on delay was temporary and that a future serious flood—as was to occur in December, 1975—could not only lead to a dam being built but to the environmentalists being blamed for damages and injuries. The focus became 'How do we provide some level of flood control, ensure the continued economic viability of the farmers and the towns, and build the kind of land use plans and controls that maintain the valley as a greenbelt with broad recreational value?' "

Many favorable factors led to the Snoqualmie agreement. Analysis of some of these factors follows.

Parties. The dispute had continued for 15 years and parties were to some extent aligned and organized. In sequence, mediators had to (a) gain the Governor's approval to investigate mediation's potential, (b) establish credibility and trust with the parties, and (c) select negotiating representatives who could carry their groups. Each of the three steps was facilitated by the stage of the dispute and the previous formation of parties.

Stage of dispute. All parties had experienced the problems that delays in settlement can cause (e.g., flood damage, expense, time, frustration, uncertainty). The dispute was in its middle-to-later stages and cried for attention. It was clear that if those advocating development of the dam pressed forward unilaterally, lawsuits could be initiated later by those opposed. However, at the time mediation was being considered no grounds existed for any lawsuits. In short, mediation looked promising, was accepted, and delivered.

Resolution Efforts

Role of the third party. Governor Dan Evans, a former engineer, was originally opposed to the Corps plan for two dams on the upper reaches of the river. He encouraged the entrance of mediators into the dispute, however. Cormick formally offered mediation services in a proposal presented to Evans by a pro-dam official in the Washington Department of Ecology, a move which fostered cooperation between pro- and anti-dam factions from the start. Evans quickly endorsed the mediation effort, followed its progress with interest, and gave a hearty endorsement to the outcome.

Funding for the mediators. Funding was derived from the independent Ford and Rockefeller Foundations, committing the mediators financially to no party. Parties could therefore trust the impartiality of the intervenors.

Compromise plans. The Snoqualmie effort was also successful because several compromise plans existed for flood control and recreation on the river. As many as four plans and combinations of them were considered before final agreement was reached.

Mediability

The Snoqualmie effort clearly demonstrates the efficacy of mediation in a well-researched and carefully chosen environmental conflict situation. It must be emphasized that much background work was done before Snoqualmie could be determined suitable for mediation, and that the perseverance, skills, and personalities of Cormick and McCarthy and their support staff played a key role in the negotiation process. The mediators place most credit with the negotiators, many of whom worked long days at their regular jobs and then attended negotiation sessions until well into the night.

It should also be noted that, prior to negotiations, an impasse had been reached after years of frustration (see Fig. 8). Realization of a common focus and diligent work by all involved finally produced a settlement. And the press greeted the settlement enthusiastically, in one case even terming it a "miracle" agreement (*Seattle Times*, 1974). At last word all parties were satisfied, and the compromise solution was being implemented.

In sum, this was a remarkable, pioneering effort in the use of mediation techniques for resolution of environmental conflicts.

KICKAPOO RIVER (WISCONSIN)

Setting

Geographic scale. The controversy over construction of a dam and impoundment on the Kickapoo River is in many ways parallel to the Snoqualmie case. Issues of flood control, recreation, and preservation of a unique botanical and geological area in southwestern Wisconsin (Fig. 9) are among those that were debated by the parties to this dispute. Actions of the Corps of Engineers and former Governor Patrick Lucey of Wisconsin are of special note in comparison to those of Governor Evans and the Corps concerning Snoqualmie.

Parties. The Kickapoo case involves not only the residents of the river basin, Lucey, his staff, other Wisconsin officials, and the Corps, but the Congressional power of Wisconsin Senators William Proxmire and Gaylord Nelson. Proxmire is a ranking member of the Senate Appropriations Committee, which authorizes funds for Corps projects.

Stage of dispute. After months of complicated negotiations between the two senators concerning project goals, alternative flood control studies, and the correct political prescription for the people of the Kickapoo basin and of Wisconsin, a compromise was finally reached that funds be allotted for a study of alternatives to a dam and impoundment. During these months the project was alternately active and inactive, criticized for being too costly and promoted as being necessary for valley residents, and supported and reproved—often by the same party.

Resolution Efforts

Role of the third party. Governor Lucey appeared to play a sort of mediation role in the Kickapoo controversy. During the period 1971-1974, Lucey had offered conditional support for the project on the basis of his assessment of local needs. He did, however, warn the Corps in 1974 that removal of trees at the site should be delayed until final water quality studies were analyzed. In May of 1975 Lucey withdrew his support because of reports and opinions from various authoritative sources which stated that water quality in the impoundment would be poor. He was joined in opposition to the project later in the year by the Wisconsin Department of Natural Resources and Senator Proxmire. Senator Nelson had long favored a moratorium on construction until studies of alternative flood control measures were completed.

Compromise plans. Wisconsin Rep. Alvin Baldus, one of the major proponents of the dam and impoundment project, finally joined the other Wisconsin officials in a unified position on Kickapoo in January, 1976. A joint letter was sent at that time by Lucey, Proxmire, Nelson, and Baldus to Congressional

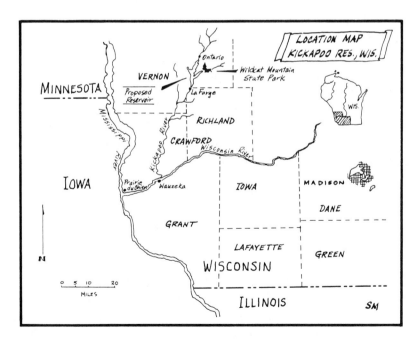

Fig. 9

Appropriations Committees; the letter requested the Corps to study options such as a dry dam without recreational lake, evacuation and relocation of buildings, and combinations of other types of flood control. A unified, compromise position on the project was considered necessary in order to insure financial support for the studies. Implementation of the Corps study was underway as of May, 1976.

A local citizen's group from Madison, Wisconsin, the Wisconsin Inland Waterways Association, learned of Cormick's work in Washington and proposed mediation of the Kickapoo dispute to Governor Lucey in 1975. Apparently the Governor declined.

The Corps had previously taken the lead in implementation because of its initial conception of the project and its responsibility for acquiring development funds. When a compromise was finally reached, the Corps was the logical choice to carry out the various flood control studies.

Mediability

In spite of the fact that overt mediation was not used in the Kickapoo case, the dispute was suitable for mediation. Components of the conflict—issues, interested parties, size of the conflict arena, and affected agencies—were right. Lucey appeared receptive to the mediation idea, and the final agreement was similar to the Snoqualmie settlement. The urgent need for a unified position to insure funding caused the parties to this dispute to use the negotiation/mediation process without a recognized outside intervenor.

LOCK AND DAM 26, MISSISSIPPI RIVER (ILLINOIS)

Setting

The environmental conflict over proposed improvement of Lock and Dam 26 on the Mississippi River at Alton, Illinois (Fig. 10) is instructive because of its potential magnitude and its impact on U.S. transportation policy. A curious alliance of opponents has been organized on the one side, while on the

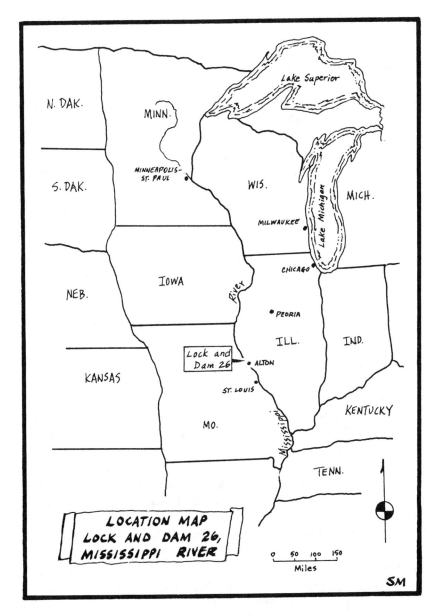

Fig. 10

other the Corps of Engineers is pressing for a project that could determine its strength and prestige for many years to come.

The Corps proposed to improve Lock and Dam 26 with a $400 million refurbishment (which even the Corps conceded was a large project), deepening the navigable channel of the river from 9 to 12 feet and creating a larger lock to expedite barge traffic. The Corps position is that its goal is simply to maintain and operate existing waterways in good condition, and it cites this responsibility under a 1909 law. The argument has not, however, met with great favor in the courtroom battles over Lock and Dam 26 during 1975-1976.

Parties. Opposing the Corps is a coalition of environmental groups and midwestern railroad companies. The alliance is curious because environmental and other private interest groups rarely join in environmental conflicts. They often aim at different goals. In this case, however, the coalition contends that the proposed 12-foot channel at Alton is part of a grand scheme, perhaps ultimately totalling $7-10 billion, to greatly improve and enlarge the capability for barge traffic on the total Mississippi River system. The coalition argues that the U.S. government, through the Corps, is proposing to subsidize barge traffic and further revitalize waterborne commerce at the expense of the mostly private investment in railroads. Specific environmental objections center on the disposal of a projected 10 million cubic yards of sand and rock that would have to be dredged initially, and on the effects of the dredged material on fish and wildlife in the river ecosystems. Other issues are comparisons of energy efficiency and environmental impacts between rail traffic, highway traffic, and waterborne commerce.

Geographic scale. The geographic scale of this conflict approaches that of the Reserve Mining case. Alliance of midwestern railroad companies with representatives of natural environmental groups certainly gives the dispute a regional scope, and possibly a national one.

Stage of dispute. The final decision on Lock and Dam 26 could well set a precedent for Corps projects on the entire Mississippi River system and could affect Corps planning efforts throughout the country. A decision favorable either to the Corps or to the railroads would constitute a *regulatory* decision according to Lowi (1964; see Hart, 1974, for discussion), in which a policy confers benefits to specified parties while depriving other parties in the process. This case falls short, however, of the largest *redistributive* category that Lowi discusses, in which society-wide classes are burdened and benefitted (e.g., income tax policies alternately benefit and burden various economic segments of society, according to public complaints by the rich, the poor and the middle class).

Resolution Efforts

Each of the three groups of contestants—the Corps, the railroads, and the environmentalists—has much to lose if a settlement is unfavorable to its interests. Frustrated in the courts, the Corps has gone to Congress for its approval, which would be embodied in an appropriation for the project by federal legislators. At last word the prospect of Congressional approval was meeting with some difficulties.

Mediability

The presence of the railroads in the Lock and Dam 26 dispute and the effect of any decision on the Corps and on national transportation policy would seem to discourage the use of mediation by an impartial third party. The conflict has been highly politicized. Informal mediation by the Executive Office of the President, with administrators of federal agencies, railroad and barge officials, and environmentalists as negotiators is a possibility. A Presidential assistant or federal administrator might then announce the settlement in the form of a policy decision.

Land Resources

PROJECT SEAFARER (MICHIGAN)

Setting

Geographic scale. Project Seafarer, formerly known as Project Sanguine (and, in 1979, known as Project ELF), has been proposed for several areas throughout the United States since the U.S. Navy first initiated it in 1958. The project involves construction of an underground grid (at a depth of four to six feet) for one-way communication with nuclear submarines. Extremely Low Frequency (ELF) radio waves would be used for communications purposes. The proposed cable grid would underlie approximately 2,400 square miles in a sparsely populated area west of Marquette, Michigan on the Upper Peninsula (UP) between Lake Superior and the northern Wisconsin border (Fig. 11).

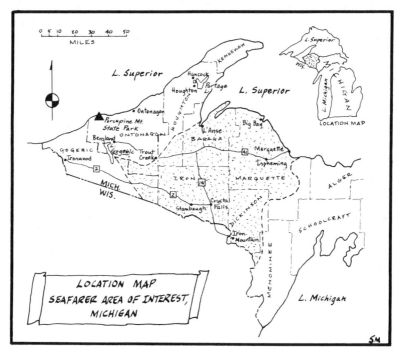

Fig. 11

Seafarer presents a curious environmental conflict because, although many states have been involved, the impacts of proposed development will benefit and cost primarily that portion of that state (an area compromising several counties by most state standards) where it is built. Externalities, or costs and benefits for which no compensation exists, are present here as in all environmental disputes, but to a lesser extent than in the other case studies surveyed because of the nature of proposed development. Of course, benefits of expenditures for the national defense are large-scale and often controversial externalities.

Seafarer also says something about the public view of "pork barrel" projects, which were, prior to 1970, generally used by Congressmen to win favor among their constituents. Such projects promised and delivered jobs, revenue and economic revitalization; their aftermath, however, may have aided the cause of environmental legislation in the 1970s.

Parties. The benefits of Project Seafarer are economic and military, say its proponents. Estimates have varied, but Navy sources have predicted that Seafarer would employ 600 construction workers during the building phase and 100 civilians and 90 military personnel on a permanent basis. Militarily, the ELF radio waves that Seafarer generates are to be used to contact nuclear submarines submerged hundreds of feet in the ocean—a key deterrent to a nuclear attack, according to the Navy. One UP booster for Seafarer appealed to patriotism and military expertise, arguing that if the Navy's experts say Seafarer is necessary and choose the site, that choice should override local objections (Cota, 1975).

As one might guess, environmental objections to Seafarer are substantial if not well-documented. So much uncertainty surrounds the effects of the radio waves on plants, wildlife, and humans that referenda in UP cities have continually opposed Seafarer by wide margins, notwithstanding the proposed economic benefits. Moreover, opponents suggest that Seafarer would make the UP a target area in a nuclear war. The public in this case is aware of (or at least wary of) environmental impacts of the Seafarer development, a fact which can be attributed to the impact of NEPA, other environmental legislation, and the environmental education efforts of public and private agents. Although isolated relative to much of the United States, the UP is challenging Seafarer with the help of improved communications and the organized efforts of national environmental groups.

Stage of dispute. Among the states that the Navy has considered for Seafarer are Utah, Wisconsin, Texas, Michigan, Nevada and New Mexico. Favorable cost estimates are the major reasons given for reconsideration of a site in the Michigan-Wisconsin area. The project was the subject of much controversy in Wisconsin about 1970, and was rejected through a concentrated effort by environmentalists and Wisconsin Senators Nelson and Proxmire. The Upper Peninsula of Michigan, however, possesses similar low-conductivity bedrock to that of northern Wisconsin, allowing close spacing of cables and a reduction in construction costs from about $550 million in the Southwestern states to about $250 million in the Great Lakes state.

In 1974, the proponents of Seafarer looked seriously at politically conservative Utah as a project site. The Navy hoped to generate support for economic benefits of the project while outmaneuvering any environmental opposition. Plans for project development in Utah apparently did not materialize, perhaps to the ultimate benefit of the Navy. Utah citizens, like those of the Upper Peninsula of Michigan, have experienced a rise in environmental consciousness (see Kaiparowits case in the Air Resources section of this chapter).

Resolution Efforts

The actions of Michigan's governor, William G. Milliken, deserve study in the Seafarer case. Milliken once said that his own position on the project was negative, but he invited the Navy to study the Michigan site in September, 1975, with a caution that this invitation should not be regarded as an opportunity to justify or "sell" the proposal to study area residents. He later expressed dissatisfaction with the Navy's effort, however, deeming it a "selling" of the project rather than a legitimate information process. Milliken appears to have wanted to give the Navy and Michigan a fair chance at Seafarer, but presently is responding to public pressure against the project. He also appeared surprised at the negative UP reaction in referenda.

It should be noted that, by mid-1976, Wisconsin's two highly visible senators, Gaylord Nelson and William Proxmire, had joined with the two Michigan senators and Michigan Rep. Philip Ruppe (long indecisive on the project) to oppose Seafarer publicly.

An update of this case study to June, 1979, shows the dispute continuing but perhaps near resolution by the President. Known as Project ELF and with a new, reduced configuration (130 miles of antenna to link to a Clam Lake, Wisconsin, test facility, instead of Seafarer's 2400 miles of antenna), the proposal is still causing controversy. Northern Wisconsin and Upper Michigan residents are actively debating the potential merits and hazards, with scientific, technical, and political disagreement evident.

The Seafarer configuration was cancelled by the President following publication of the project's final impact statement in December, 1977. The ELF proposal has earmarked funds in the federal fiscal year 1979 budget process, but their status is uncertain. According to Navy sources (Hoshko, 1979), Congress has specified that no ELF funds be spent until the President approves the project. He is scheduled to make his decision in mid-1979, and that decision is predicted both ways, depending upon the source.

Mediability

The Seafarer dispute could have benefitted from environmental mediation. A mediator could have acted as facilitator and communicator between parties, in order that the interested but indecisive UP and northern Wisconsin residents could feel they were getting accurate information endorsed by both sides. Had the project been approved in some form by negotiators representing the parties, the mediator could have continued the facilitation process, minimizing distrust and polarization.

To illustrate, an information gap occurred when the Navy, after facing initial opposition to the project in Wisconsin,

announced that a "technological breakthrough" allowed reduction of the proposed grid size from 26 counties to 8. Similar
events have occurred in Michigan and Wisconsin to antagonize
residents. It follows that if Seafarer/ELF is to be approved by
the President in some form anywhere in the United States,
negotiation of project configuration, location of supporting
facilities, and other factors could make development acceptable to affected parties.

BOUNDARY WATERS CANOE AREA (MINNESOTA)

Setting

Geographic scale. The dispute concerning the Boundary
Waters Canoe Area (BWCA) in northern Minnesota (Fig. 12)
is comparable to that of Project Seafarer but has a special
feature. That feature is the designation of a portion of the
BWCA as wilderness area, signifying national interest in this
northern land of lakes and forests. The wilderness designation
and the different perceptions of two interests concerned with
natural resources—environmental groups and the U.S. Forest
Service—have presented a philosophical contradiction to those
who would try to resolve this conflict.

Parties. Enactment of the Wilderness Act of 1964 meant
immediate designation of 10 million acres of the United States
as wilderness area, restricted for use and preserved as an
enclave for the footprints and thoughts of all concerned with
conservation of natural resources. Wilderness Society and
USFS spokesmen agree that insufficient acreage has been re-
served as wilderness since 1964 (only 1.5-2 million acres).
However, these two parties cannot agree on which policies
shall govern the use of wilderness once it is set aside. The
Forest Service advocates multiple use (lumbering with controlled burning in some cases, and recreational uses that may
involve motorboats and snowmobiles), while the Wilderness
Society urges only primitive camping to include such quiet,
passive uses as canoeing and cross-country skiing.

The 1-million acre BWCA is no longer an idyllic, isolated,
little-used wilderness. Canoeists must now apply for reserva-

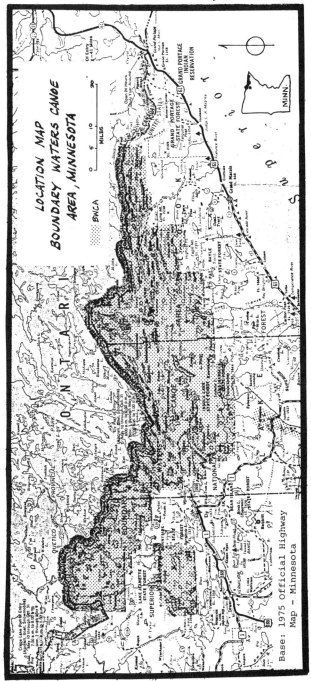

Fig. 12

tions, enter and leave the area on certain dates, and travel from campsite to campsite on a prearranged schedule. Nonetheless, for the 163,000 visitors to the BWCA in 1974, their experience was extremely gratifying.

Stage of dispute. Litigation of this dispute began when environmental groups (including Minnesota Public Interest Research Group and the Sierra Club) commenced an action against logging by USFS in November, 1972. Since that time the case has been heard by Judge Miles Lord of Reserve Mining fame, whose opinions have tended to disfavor the USFS position. The litigation currently continues. Before litigation commenced, however, compromises were proposed to USFS by the environmental groups for cancellation of some logging areas, modifications in size of other areas, and other matters. These efforts were "continually rebuffed," and in the opinion of one lawyer representing the environmental groups (Dayton, 1976), mediation is not feasible here because of the philosophical split.

Resolution Efforts

Role of the third party. There are hints of compromise in news reports, however. U.S. Rep. James Oberstar is acting as a mediator of sorts by introducing legislation to balance the use of the BWCA between economic and environmental interests.

Compromise plans. Oberstar is attempting a compromise by partially satisfying each side, while making the total package larger. The primitive wilderness area would, in Oberstar's proposal, encompass over 600,000 acres and the multiple use area just over 500,000 acres, increasing the total size of BWCA by over 100,000 acres. The Sierra Club has indicated that it is willing to work with Oberstar to settle by law the future use of BWCA, and a representative of the Northern Environmental Council, another party to the dispute, called Oberstar's bill a realistic approach toward the compromise that will ultimately resolve the BWCA controversy.

Mediability

As long as court decisions can further one interest or the other and philosophical principles remain intact, the opportunity for mediation of BWCA seems negligible. But legal findings have supported first one policy and then another. Oberstar has emerged as a mediator who, through the legislative process, is attempting to implement what he believes is an acceptable compromise. He seems to be acting as facilitator, communicator, and implementer in a third party sense. It appears that a negotiation/mediation process is producing resolution in this case.

Oberstar could undoubtedly be assisted in his conciliation effort by an outside mediator who could facilitate communication between parties and extract realistic expectations and desires for settlement and implementation of that settlement from those involved. BWCA has a number of attributes that make it a potentially mediable dispute. Representative Oberstar's work enhances the prospects for mediation.

Air Resources

AEROSOL CANS

Setting

Conflicts involving use of the atmosphere present a puzzling set of cases for the environmental mediator. As difficult as impact boundaries may be to define in land and water pollution controversies, the impact of air pollution is even more complex. Congress and the courts have had continuing difficulty in dealing with air quality regions, ambient air quality standards, and nondegradation of clean air. Air is not nearly so captive as water or land; controversies involving its use create problems for the mediator.

Geographic scale. The controversy concerning aerosol cans is typical of those involving air pollution on a large scale. Some believe that man-made freon, the propellant most commonly used in aerosol cans, is depleting the earth's ozone layer as the freon rises to the earth's upper atmosphere. A depleted ozone layer could mean that greater than normal amounts of ultraviolet radiation would reach the earth, causing an increased incidence of skin cancer. The issue is still being debated.

Parties. The public is acting as the mediator of this environmental dispute. Everyone who is a potential user of aerosols is free to decide whether to use them or not. Industrial policy concerning aerosol production is *distributive,* as defined by Lowi (again, see Hart for discussion). The market governs which products will be produced and purchased, in spite of the feelings by many that markets manipulate people and coerce them to buy products they do not want or need. Production of aerosol cans as *distributive* policy confers highly divisible benefits upon particular groups (aerosol can workers, their families, and the corporations who hire them), and allegedly burdens or harms the general public through depletion of a limited resource, the ozone layer.

Stage of dispute. There is a growing trend by manufacturers to phase out aerosol cans because the public will not buy them—or, as one report puts it, they are leaving "ssst" and going back to "ffft". Media advertising reinforces the trend. The market has served to mediate the controversy.

Mediability

From this description, it is obvious that an environmental mediator (or team of mediators) has no place in a controversy such as that involving aerosol propellants. The mediator might make a few observations, however. For instance, parties to the dispute show disproportionate numbers and strengths. The arena of conflict and settlement is very large, and the ultimate decision-makers are those controlling industrial policies, including federal agency administrators and the Executive Office of the President if the federal government chooses to regulate aerosols. Divisble benefits of continued production are present as in the Reserve Mining Case, but the alleged harm in the aerosol situation is more widespread. A reasonable alternative exists for consumers and conditions are favorable for a change in consumer behavior.

KAIPAROWITS POWER PLANT (UTAH)

Setting

Parties. The environmental conflict regarding proposed construction of a power plant on the Kaiparowits plateau in southern Utah (see Fig. 13) is a typical one for the western

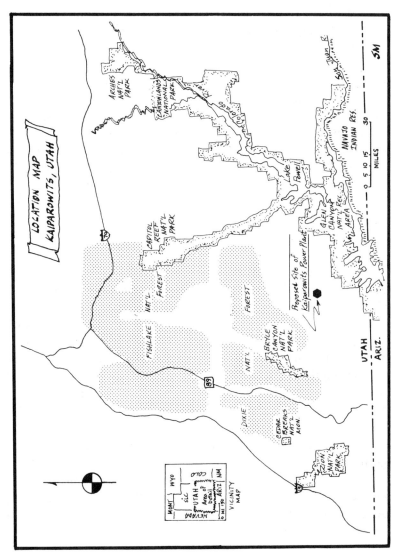

Fig. 13

United States. The proposed 3,000 megawatt coalfired plant was planned to burn an estimated 8 million tons of local coal each year; cooling water was to be taken from nearby Lake Powell. The power was to supply growing urban areas of Arizona and Southern California. Utilities and those favoring the economic benefits of the plant aligned themselves against environmentalists, who protested the impacts of air pollution, aesthetic deterioration, strip mining, and water diversions on several contiguous national parks, forests, monuments, and recreation areas.

This region is a theatre for environmental controversy. Construction of the Glen Canyon Dam, resulting in Lake Powell, and the subsequent flooding of Rainbow Bridge National Monument by the lake both created conflict in past years. Local environmental groups were therefore organized and ready to meet the challenge of Kaiparowits. They had the benefit of support (and resultant favorable, nationwide television coverage) from a well-known motion picture actor, and the backing and attention of national environmental groups. The usual interests supported plant construction—utilities, local bankers, businessmen, and blue collar workers.

Geographic scale. This case study is discussed in the air resources section in order to pose a contrast to the conflict over aerosol cans. Although the possible impacts of atmospheric pollution are difficult to determine, Kaiparowits would allegedly have the capacity to pollute the air over eight national parks and three national recreation areas (within a 200-mile radius of the plant site) with up to 300 tons/day of atmospheric contaminants (Hill, 1976). Emissions would have exceeded permissible limits if these park lands were to be classified as atmospheric nondegradation areas under the Clean Air Act Amendments of 1970. Consequently, conservationists had a precedent-setting issue of great importance, since the nondegradation clause (which simply means keeping clean air clean) is being hotly debated throughout the country by industrialists and environmentalists. Air pollution in this case could be allegedly related to areas with definite boundaries, including areas of national significance.

Stage of dispute. The Kaiparowits project has been abandoned by the utilities. News of the demise of Kaiparowits was as startling to environmentalists as it was to almost everyone else involved. Utah Governor Calvin Rampton, who supported the project early on because of the estimated 8,800 potential jobs and $130 million in salaries and revenues which could be generated by 1986, was aware of the growing costs and unreasonably long delay that the project faced. Nevertheless, he viewed the outcome as a blow to attempts of the United States to attain energy independence. He admitted, however, that the decision was a victory for the concept that one state should not bear the costs of developing and exporting its natural resources with few benefits in return.

Resolution efforts

At first glance, few mediable aspects and few compromises present themselves in the Kaiparowits case. But was the choice a simple one of building the plant or not building it? A few clues to what we might term "indirect compromise" are present. Southern California Edison (SCE), one of the major utilities in the consortium which proposed Kaiparowits, noted that any near-term needs for the plant's cancelled output would have to be met by "combined cycle" generating plants, which burn a type of kerosene and which can be built more quickly than coal-fired plants. For the long term, SCE is looking to triple the nuclear generating capacity on the California coast at San Onofre.

Mediability

The mediator in this dispute might have suggested negotiable, ancillary aspects of the dispute that could have produced settlement. It is probably fortunate for all involved that Kaiparowits is (for now) finished. Utilities can get on with their business and preservationists can enjoy, in thought or in person, the benefits of wilderness lands in southern Utah. This particular analysis of indirect compromise suggests, however, that Kaiparowits will resurface in disguise sometime, somewhere.

Human Resources

AESTHETICS AND QUALITY OF LIFE

Issues of aesthetics and quality of life arise more often now than they did ten years ago. The average citizen is becoming aware that what he sees, smells, touches, breathes, and hears while at work and at play influence his quality of life. Some things make life more pleasurable and enjoyable, producing a feeling of satisfaction and contentment that lasts hours, days, or even years. Other sensations make our quality of life decidedly less pleasurable—excessive noises or odors, foul air, and unpleasant, garish sights that offer no visual beauty.

Results of various studies of quality of life in the United States have come to public attention in the past few years. Cities and states have been ranked not just for their physical attributes but for their cultural, political, and social conditions. Development of natural resources influences aesthetics and quality of life most directly as it changes the physical environment. The physical environment in turn has some influences on social conditions; in combination, a generally pleasing or displeasing quality of life exists in a particular area.

DEVELOPMENT AND ENVIRONMENTAL CONFLICT
IN SMALL COMMUNITIES

Environmental conflicts created by the physical effects of development are sometimes difficult to assess in large metropolitan areas. New York City, Chicago, and Los Angeles can absorb countless small injuries to their physical and social environments before the cumulative effects are evident. But small towns and cities are often directly and permanently harmed (and benefitted) by development.

To illustrate, larger cities can absorb the few hundreds of population that a new industry may bring with little social upheaval, and can handle growth more easily than can small communities because of their often well-developed capabilities for planning and police power. Relatively unpopulated areas may experience severe ecological impact but little social impact, because few people are there to be affected by development. A human settlement of modest population size which is experiencing rapid changes in population because of industrial development may, however, suffer serious and detrimental impacts on both its environment and its social structure. The town is usually at the mercy of the industry economically; and, increasingly in this decade of the '70s, the industry faces environmental regulation that can, in turn, affect the town. A town and its industry can therefore experience a painful period of stress, and eventual collapse.

The small community is ripe for community involvement and controversy over an environmental issue. As previously discussed, Coleman (1957: 3-10) noted that events inspire conflict when they touch people's lives, affect parties differently and are susceptible to active response. Differences in economic structure, changes in pace of events, population shifts, heterogeneous values, and existing cleavages may create favorable conditions for conflict. The nature of the conflict itself can change from specific to general, one issue to many, and disagreement to antagonism.

Environmental conflicts in small towns necessarily involve issues such as air, water, and land pollution. The small community case studies are presented in this section to illustrate the social impacts of development on small towns. These impacts are repeated many times each year in the United States, as small towns feel the local growing pains of laws, policies, and developments of a much broader scope. Following are some examples of environmental disputes in small communities. As in previous sections, a "moment in time" analysis will be used current to the period January-May, 1976.

Mining in the Western United States is gaining importance as mineral resources become scarce and as the energy shortage demands development of coal, uranium, and oil reserve. *Rock Springs, in southwest Wyoming,* experienced an influx of about 5,000 new workers in 1971 for construction of the Jim Bridger Power Plant. A 1974 report predicted that other mineral development would cause an increase in Rock Springs population from 26,000 in that year to 40,000 by 1976. Business interests are of course jubilant, but mixed blessings are evident. Schools are overcrowded, traffic jams prevalent, unsavory characters accompany the boom, and the crime rates and numbers of mental health problems are rising. The boom and bust cycle also threatens Gillette, situated near large, easily accessible coal seams in the northeast part of the state. The attendant problems are not now so romantic and easily solved as they were one hundred years ago.

Butte, Montana (pop. 24,000) and neighboring *Anaconda* (pop. 10,000) are mining towns experiencing different but equally threatening problems. Butte and Anaconda are both Anaconda Copper Co. (ACC) towns, whose residents rode the prosperous times of the mid-1900s when ore reserves were high, prices good, and environmental concerns neglected or not pressing enough to matter. The city of Butte is now threatened by ACC's right of eminent domain (negotiated when the town was founded), which allows the company to buy up any surface property which stands in the way of operations. The town's residential and business districts are being encroached upon as ore becomes scarce, since Butte is built on a mineral-rich hill. If ACC stopped operations and moved out, 3,000 people would be out of work. Relocation of the business district could cost $1.5 million. A group of community leaders are now trying to deal with Butte's problems.

Anaconda is feeling a different impact from its copper production. The world's largest smokestack (585 feet tall) in Anaconda's smelter symbolizes employment to 5,000 Montana residents and financial support for most of the townspeople. But smoke from the smelter stack may also mean high rates of lung cancer and respiratory disease for area residents because of arsenic emitted during the smelting process. Wives and families of the smelter workers are affected in addition to the workers. But what is a smelter worker with limited education, a family to support, and a comfortable income and situation expected to do? It is easy to suggest that the family move and find work elsewhere, but is it practical? Attendant to the conflict the town faces are proposed EPA standards for air pollutant emissions. Environmental versus economic health for Anaconda residents is the major issue here—the phrase "pollution means jobs" aptly characterizes the dilemma.

The village of *Aurora, N.C.* (pop. 671) faces social problems from nearby phosphate mining operations. Phosphate is used in fertilizer production and is of increasing importance because of current world food shortages. Beaufort County, surrounding Aurora, contains one of the world's richest deposits. Here Texasgulf, the development corporation, has ownership rights similar to those of Anaconda Copper at Butte. As mining operations on company-owned land come closer and closer to the city limits, conflict is developing between area leaders and the company over the deterioration of a town which saw the promise of prosperity when Texasgulf first began operations.

In the case of Aurora, Texasgulf officials allegedly predicted that the town would boom to a population of 15,000 at the height of phosphate mining operations. Instead, land use changes occurred because many small farmers sold out and only a few hundred people moved in. The town's social and economic structure is deteriorating. Texasgulf is contributing economically and politically to Aurora, but the price is high in terms of a deteriorating quality of life in Beaufort County.

The community of *Chippewa Falls, Wis.* (pop. 11,700) has experienced conflict over operation of a meat-packing plant. Air pollution from the plant has caused bad odors and has diminished the quality of life for community residents. The company, however, points to the $5 million annual payroll, $3 million tax base, and 400 jobs it supplies to this heretofore economically depressed community. At last word the community was demanding curtailment of operations, and the local Chamber of Commerce was suggesting that further operations be allowed only on condition that the plant will comply with air pollution standards.

The preservation of Long Island farmland in predominantly rural *Suffolk County, New York* illustrates a land use problem of increasing importance in the United States. In order for the rural land to be protected from speculators, a $60 million bond issue would be floated to cover the cost of a program to purchase the land and allow farmers to continue working it. Support for the bond issue is needed from urban as well as from rural residents.

Another environmental conflict (introduced in Chapter Five) involves construction of a barley malting plant in an industrial park in *Moorhead, Minn.* (pop. 40,000). Economic benefits of the plant are offset by the concern of the Minnesota Public Interest Research Group that an environmental impact statement be required to assess water and wastewater requirements of the project. Anheuser-Busch, the proponent, was reportedly considering an alternative plant site in nearby Fargo, North Dakota, because of the potential $100,000-$200,000 cost and the 6-18 month time requirement for EIS preparation in Minnesota. An impasse was reached before mediation allowed the parties to communicate and the project is proceeding in Moorhead (Fradin, 1976).

Proposals for mining of copper (and possibly iron ore) near the *northwest Wisconsin town of Ladysmith* (pop. 3,600) are gaining much attention. Some local residents and the state legislators who represent them are determined not to allow Kennecott Copper, the major development firm, to make millions in profit per year while Rusk County receives a comparatively small royalty. Other local residents welcome the substantial increase in income that the mining operation will bring to the community. Several small cities in southwestern and northern Wisconsin face similar dilemmas by reason of recent discoveries of lead, zinc, copper, nickel, and iron ore throughout the state and the potential development of these resources in response to scarcity of metals and rising prices. Degradation of the physical environment is a concern, but this concern is being mitigated by existing regulations and policies. The social impacts of location of ancillary structures (e.g. smelters) and provision of housing and community services for incoming workers and their families are a greater concern. Negotiation of such secondary issues might allow development of a mining operation in a manner satisfactory to most local interests.

PRELIMINARY CONCLUSIONS—
SUITABILITY OF DISPUTES FOR MEDIATION

The case studies in this chapter show that some disputes will obviously lend themselves to mediation and that others will not. However, some introductory comments may be instructive before disputes are categorized as generally mediable or not mediable.

The disputes surveyed in this chapter vary in terms of geographic scale and stage of conflict. Some are small in geographic scale, involving local decisions and conditions, and have not, as yet, captured national attention. Others encompass small communities but have generated national interest— their story is told in national wire service dispatches and television documentaries. Large-scale disputes generally gain great exposure because of their magnitudes and impacts.

Similarly, disputes are differentiated by their stages of conflict. Some have just begun, or may be about to begin when a sufficient number of people realize that a problem exists which demands a future solution. Other conflicts are well-established, defined through months or even years of antagonism and frustration. Still others are at impasse: they too are well-established, but are at such a stage of conflict that their continuance may mean great costs in terms of mental and physical health, damages to natural resources, human property, or even human lives. And finally, a common circumstance in conflict stages is for a dispute to be, as Bilder puts it, "largely overtaken by events." In other words, certain actions or conditions may have engulfed the dispute, enlarging its scope, clouding the issues, and disguising the nature of a proper settlement.

Other, specific observations on the case studies deserve further discussion.

(a) *Conclusions on mediability.* Some conflicts are large-scale, expensive, "classic" cases. The Reserve Mining case concerns environment and employment in a small town, but the case is international in scope because of the legal precedents it will establish, because of the international corporation party to the dispute, and because of the impacts of the ultimate Reserve decision on world steel production. The Reserve case has been reported by the national wire services, national television networks, and national newsmagazines. Of course, the Anaconda, Montana, or Aurora, North Carolina, cases may reach the proportions of Reserve in terms of geographic scale and public recognition. *Conflicts like Reserve are often "largely overtaken by events,"* and are settled only after intervention by federal agency administrators or the Executive Office of the President.

(b) *Cases in which environmental mediation has been successful possess common attributes.* Both the Snoqualmie and the Moorhead cases were favorable for mediation in terms of the alignment of parties, stage of conflict, independent funding for mediator(s), and available compromise plans for development

(c) *Cases of small to medium proportions* (comparable to Snoqualmie or Moorhead) *generally appear suitable for mediation.* The arena of conflict in such cases is local to substate regional to statewide in scope. *Favorable and unfavorable attributes for mediation can be assessed in a preliminary fashion by comparison to successful mediation efforts.*

(d) *Environmental conflicts involving small towns generally lend themselves to mediation for several reasons:*

(i) The dispute setting, parties, and issues are usually well defined and confined to a small geographic area. Often a lack of communication precipitates the extreme positions which seem to magnify the conflict and create an apparent impasse.

(ii) Negotiable, ancillary aspects of the dispute are often obvious, and settlement of ancillary issues can lead to compromise and settlement of the total conflict.

(iii) In spite of their usually undeveloped capacity for planning and plan implementation, local governments are able to implement solutions more easily than larger governments with many constituents. Fewer people in small, defined geographic areas make for simple implementation once agreement is reached.

(iv) The opportunity for human solutions (see discussion in Hardin, 1968) to solve a conflict is apparent and easily implemented in small geographic areas. In contrast, most New York City residents could not be easily educated as to the environmentally valuable effects of keeping Suffolk County rural.

(v) Such disputes are generally community/ environmental disputes. Conflict may have arisen over racial discrimination in addition to the use of natural resources (e.g., Indian claims to native lands now owned or used by whites). Ideological, economic, and racial issues may be analyzed in conjunction with environmental issues in circumstances like these; in addition, one may consult the substantial literature on community conflict.

Specific opportunities for compromise and settlement are present in the small community case studies described previously: A potential compromise between the town planning board and Texasgulf officials is reported concerning the Aurora conflict (Nelsen, 1976). Compliance with emission standards and a diligent search for an arsenic market by Anaconda Copper might provide a suitable compromise for Anaconda, Montana. The report on the Chippewa Falls, Wisconsin, dispute suggests that each side is stepping down its demands in order to reach agreement (*Milwaukee Journal,* 1975). A similar case in Madison, Wisconsin is currently (June 1979) being mediated by the Wisconsin Center for Public Policy's Environmental Mediation Project. At issue is the odor caused by the emissions from a meat-packing plant. Fradin (1976) reports that communications between parties led to compromise in the Moorhead case. Further, these small community case stud ies (and several others examined) suggest and support the conclusions on mediability stated above.

Suitability for mediation in the case studies in this chapter is determined on the basis of past, present, or potential future attributes of the disputes. Mediation as a mechanism for settlement would be likely to occur through intervention by an impartial third party. Mediation does not, however, preclude the use of compromise and negotiation/mediation techniques by a legislator, state official, or other person already party to the dispute. The key prerequisites for a mediated settlement are that it be accomplished out-of-court and away from formalized, administrative procedures, and that mediation be an extraordinary process which carries with it a commitment to implement the solution (Cormick, 1976: 3-6).

Dispute case studies presented in this chapter are classified into the following two groups.

SUITABLE FOR MEDIATION

Snoqualmie (already mediated)

Kickapoo

Lock and Dam 26

Seafarer

Boundary Waters Canoe Area

PCBs in Hudson

Kaiparowits

Small Communities (generally)

Moorhead Malting Plant (already mediated)

UNSUITABLE FOR MEDIATION

Reserve Mining

Aerosol Cans

Many other case studies could be considered and analyzed for amenability to mediation. The sample presented is sufficient to show similarities in dispute components.

In summary, the following attributes of environmental disputes appear to be most important in determining the suitability or unsuitability of those disputes for mediation:

(1) stage of conflict; whether an impasse has been reached;

(2) parties to dispute; their sizes and sanctions;

(3) geographic scope of the dispute;

(4) role of the state governor in the conflict;

(5) negotiable, ancillary factors that could produce settlement;

(6) social and psychological factors, notably facesaving, communicative processes, and interaction during ne-

gotiation, which the mediator could only evaluate first-hand; and

(7) means for implementation of the agreement.

Further discussion and analysis of these attributes will be presented, with illustrative examples, in the final two chapters.

VII.
Environmental Conflict Analysis Methods

In this chapter a set of questions, developed from the preceeding chapters, is proposed to allow the prospective mediator to diagnose disputes and to suggest mediation procedures. The purpose of these questions from various disciplines is to determine an approach, be it analytical, descriptive, or quantitative, which can lead to a mediator's discovery of alternative solutions, compromises, and settlements which conflicting parties could agree upon and implement.

ECONOMICS

Question 1: Is benefit/cost (B/C) analysis an important issue in the dispute? If so, are there inconsistent assumptions in the claims of each side regarding B/C analysis that could be resolved by the use of realistic examination and assessment, as facilitated by a third party?

Discussion: The U.S. Army Corps of Engineers is required to perform B/C analysis for water resources projects under provisions of the Flood Control Act of 1936, and to give evidence that benefits of the project will exceed estimated costs—i.e., the B/C ratio will be greater than 1.00. Many projects involving flood control efforts by the Corps have been criticized because of the initial Corps B/C analysis. Environmental groups have attacked B/C figures presented by the Corps primarily because of unconvincing estimates of benefits. Accrued projects benefits are difficult to determine, since services or goods produced (e.g., flood control benefits) are not sold in typical market fashion.

One of the central issues of the Lock and Dam 26 controversy was the Corps' computation of a B/C ratio. Haveman (1975), using such economic concepts as existing delay costs, real discount rates, cost savings, and accurate measures of real construction costs, has estimated that the B/C ratio for the Lock and Dam 26 project could be computed as low as .11, compared to the initial Corps' figure of 1.5. Disagreement over computation of the B/C ratio for Lock and Dam 26 can naturally influence Congressional and public opinion of the project.

What is the mediator able to do when such a controversy exists over one aspect of a project? If future repercussions on a national scale are great for two major commercial interests (railroads and barge operators), and if one side refuses to negotiate a settlement out-of-court because of the importance of the case, the mediator can do little. Such circumstances of repercussion and paralysis of negotiation do exist concerning Lock and Dam 26, at least from the point of view of the environmentalist/railroad coalition (Karaganis, 1976). Whether the Corps' (or their opponents') arguments are reasonable and have legal merit will probably be decided in a court of law.

If B/C ratios constitute a negotiable issue and if computation of them can be agreed upon, an economic compromise can be one aspect of the final settlement. The parties must agree, however, on three points: (1) what part of the disputed decision or potential decision hinges totally on B/C; (2) what the benefits are and what the costs are, and what assumptions therefore really apply; and (3) that all parties will share all information as to the levels of costs and benefits. The mediator can aid in communication and sharing of information and help to resolve the disagreements.

In addition, each disputant must agree that all ways (other than mediation) to prevail upon his own B/C justification are closed, and that mediation is the only way to achieve an acceptable solution. This last condition presupposes that both sides desire settlement.

The mediator must be cautious when dealing with disputes involving B/C analysis. Any attempts by the mediator to prevail upon the parties by imposing his own assumptions may be costly. Imposition could jeopardize one's credibility for future mediation efforts. The mediator must not cross the fine line between *facilitating* a settlement and *forcing* a settlement.

Question 2: Are analyses of the types of economic decisions involved, in terms of cause or of remedy to a particular environmental dispute, valuable for assessing the dispute for mediation?

Discussion: Writers in economics and political science have attempted to view impacts on the public welfare in terms of bargaining decisions. Dahl and Lindblom (1953: 22-24) classified bargaining decisions under four headings: (1) *hierarchy,* in which leaders control non-leaders (bureaucracy); (2) *polyarchy,* in which non-leaders control leaders (democracy); (3) *bargaining,* in which leaders control one another; and finally, (4) *market,* in which the American consumer determines resource use and policy by individual transactions.

Their definition of *market* decisions is especially useful for delimiting the types of economic decisions required to resolve major environmental disputes without third party intervention. For example, in the controversy involving fluorocarbons in aerosol cans (Chapter Six), consumers throughout the United States helped to change manufacturers' policies. Previously, a manufacturer may have attempted to market each of his new products in aerosol cans if that type of packaging was appropriate. However, during 1976 and 1977 consumer habits changed because of widespread concern about the potential harm caused by fluorocarbons, and consumers purchased fewer and fewer products in aerosol cans containing fluorocarbons. The consumers' behavior was apparently influenced by this reasoning: the benefits from the convenience of using aerosols were outweighed by the potential costs of such use in terms of threat to human health as a result of depletion of the earth's ozone layer. Manufacturers quickly sensed this reasoning as sales declined; improved hand-pumped sprays and other innovative packages were the result.

This example illustrates how elementary B/C analyses by individual consumers properly settled a major environmental dispute. The market served to mediate the conflict

Question 3: Are the continuing costs of conflict likely to force both sides to accept a settlement achieved through the negotiation/mediation process? Are side payments, penalties, effluent charges, or other compensation likely to be proposed by parties during mediation? Might such economic remedies be implemented by subsequent legislation or become the subject of future bargaining?

Discussion: Continuing conflict is costly, since delay causes (among other things) inflated construction costs as well as mental anguish and uncertainty. Commonly, the development proponent has the most to lose in terms of negotiating a compromise settlement: that proponent may not end up with its preferred plant size, location, or cost of project. But it is also common that the development proponent suffers economic losses because of continuing conflict. Construction costs rise at a rapid rate, benefits rise at a lower rate, and long-range plans may be altered to the economic detriment of the proponent. On the other side, preservation interests are usually amenable to mediation unless they desire to totally block the project and will accept no compromise. For the preservationists, compromise usually brings desirable project modifications. It follows that the mediator should ascertain what the existing conflict is costing the parties, and take advantage of the situation if it is right.

The mediator should also be aware that, during negotiations, economic remedies may be proposed to alleviate the potential costs of development. A system of effluent charges may be proposed to work in conjunction with or independently of regulatory mechanisms (although the notion of effluent charges has not gained popularity). Lump sum payments, or, to use General Electric's adjective in the Hudson River case, "good faith" penalties, may be proposed to be assessed on the alleged polluter. Side payments to compensate local residents for income lost because of potential development or nondevelopment could be discussed during environmental bargaining.

Unfortunately, the record of labor-management negotiations does not provide a list of the most mediable economic issues arising from environmental conflicts. Cormick and Patton (1977: 14), note that "while in labor-management relationships such issues as wages, management rights, and due process lend themselves to continuing review and renegotiation, environmental disputes often concern issues much less reversible, such as major construction or depletion of resources." Similarly, the economic inequities produced by development need to be remedied early on in the development process. And while these inequities are often obscure in environmental conflicts, attention to them makes for durable settlements.

The case studies in Chapter Six illustrate the economic inequities produced by development (e.g., mining in Northern Wisconsin) or non-development (e.g., wilderness areas in the Boundary Waters Canoe Area). Helgeland (1976: 98-99) has suggested that compensation to local residents, as one feature of the U.S. Forest Service plan for the Boundary Waters Canoe Area (BWCA), could have lessened the philosophcial split between local control of development and national interests for preservation. Other case studies, notably Kaiparowits and Seafarer (Chapter Six), and Mineral King in California (*Sierra Club v. Morton*, 1972), Sylvania in Michigan (Ela, 1974), and Echo Park in Colorado (Stratton and Sirotkin, 1959), repeat and emphasize the philosophical split caused by economic inequities. Appeal to a higher goal (e.g., improvement of present and future quality of life for all citizens in the locality) and discussion of economic means to achieve that goal can often lead toward agreement among tbe parties. A skillful mediator should initiate such discussion when a philosophical split threatens to bring the mediation effort to a standstill.

We must also mention broader economic notions of optimum level of pollution, assimilative capacity of the environment, and regulation of time and place of discharge to equalize costs (and discourage inequities) to the general public. Economic analysis is vital to the mediator's work, especially if one agrees that quality of life, and especially economic self-interest, has first priority in environmental conflict analysis (see Chapter Two).

LAW

Question 4: What are the prior experiences of the parties regarding litigation, and how would each party improve or weaken its position in a court trial?

Discussion: In many past environmental conflicts, an imbalance has existed between the legal resources of local environmental groups, who advocated preservation, and those of private companies and the federal government, who often were favorable to development. Pro-development interests had extensive legal staffs, budgets, and supporting resources. Consequently, pro-development interests were able in many instances to win their cases or to delay regulation to a more convenient time. Galanter (1973) has characterized the general imbalance in the legal arena as that of "one-shotters" (OS) vs. "repeat players" (RP). Galanter's diagram (Fig. 14) gives examples of various types of litigation involving OS and RP. The example "environmental preservation group v. federal agency" would have fit in block III during the early 1970s.

The mediator considering intervention can assess the experience and resources of each party relative to the other and attempt to forecast the outcome of a trial. If it appears that one side would be classified as an RP, is more powerful than its OS adversary, and is likely to win the case, that RP will probably not favor mediation. If it appears, on the other hand, that both parties are RPs familiar with the costs of litigation (in terms of loss of both time and dollars) and that the legal merits of each argument assure neither side of a favorable settlement, parties might be receptive to mediation.

The growing strength of national and state environmental groups has served to equalize legal power among preservation and development interests. For example, the National Audubon Society (NAS) has grown from approximately 264,000 members in 1973 to approximately 375,000 members in 1977 (Nye, 1977). Other experienced litigants among such groups have not grown as dramatically as NAS, but one cannot dispute the strong presence of environmental interests in every development decision.

Initiator, Claimant

	One-Shotter	**Repeat Player**
One-Shotter	Parent v. Parent (Custody) Spouse v. Spouse (Divorce) Family v. Family-Member (Insanity Commitment) Family v. Family (Inheritance) Neighbor v. Neighbor Partner v. Partner OS vs OS I	Prosecutor v. Accused Finance Co. v. Debtor I.R.S. v. Taxpayer Condemnor v. Property Owner RP vs OS II
Repeat Player	Welfare Client v. Agency Auto Dealer v. Manufacturer Injury Victim v. Insurance Company Tenant v. Landlord Bankrupt Consumer v. Creditors Defamed v. Publisher OS vs RP III	Union v. Company Movie Distributor v. Censorship Board Developer v. Surburban Municipality Purchaser v. Supplier Regulatory Agency v. Firms of Regulated Industry RP vs. RP IV

(left axis label: **Defendant**)

Fig. 14.   A taxonomy of litigation by strategic configuration of parties (after Galanter, 1973).

It follows that a relative balance of power will, as stated earlier, produce many disputes that are suitable for mediation. The Sierra Club and Environmental Defense Fund are two national groups with extensive legal expertise and experience. In the states, public interest research groups and private citizen action groups employ lawyers familiar with environmental litigation and negotiation. Coalitions of local, state, and national environmental groups have often organized to oppose development. Moreover, existing case law has clarified statutory language regarding standing to sue and the policy intent of environmental legislation.

One caveat must be entered here, as elsewhere in these discussions: *all parties* must desire mediation and a compromise settlement for the process to work. If an environmental group will advance arguments with apparent legal merit in spite of concessions by its opponent, and if that environmental group will press its legal rights to a court judgment regardless of any progress in out-of-court negotiations, the dispute is not suitable for mediation. Or, at the very least, it is not yet ripe for mediation.

Question 5: What are the other prospects for legal settlement? Is a court of law likely to decide the real-life issues of jobs, living conditions, and damages to the natural environment, or merely litigable issues? What is the status of the court calendar, the posture of the trial judge(s), and the prospect of appeal? Will a satisfactory, lasting settlement be forthcoming through legal procedures?

Discussion: Mediation has been previously compared to litigation regarding settlement of substantive issues, expense, and time needed for full adjudication (see Chapter Four). Of additional importance, if the conflict proceeds to the stage before mediation is initiated, is the record of the judge assigned to the case. Is he noted for a pro-environment or pro-business stance? For instance, the record of Judge Miles Lord in the Reserve Mining case undoubtedly influenced the parties' expectations in the BWCA litigation, over which Lord also presided. Moreover, the record of appealed cases might allow intervenors to predict the outcome if a case should go to the higher court. In the Lord example, a philosophical difference appears to exist between him and his fellow jurists in the Court of Appeals in St. Louis.

The nature of a potential legal remedy is instructive to the mediator. Will injury occur so quickly that delays from litigation will cause irreparable environmental damage? If so, and if parties are at a loss to find a legal issue on which to file suit, mediation may be feasible. Will one party press its legal rights to delay the project in litigation in spite of its opponent's apparent desire to negotiate? If so, the defendant especially may wish to negotiate using an impartial third party to mitigate delays. Will litigation specify and clarify powers in such a way that either side, being fairly equal to its opponent, may lose its potential advantage? If so, mediation may be favored, for it can perpetuate ambiguity. White (1969: 60) has noted that in some cases involving resource disputes ambiguity is desirable, for it "often averts head-on confrontations until such time as a mediating power can be found, as in the case of the long delay in clarifying divergent policies of federal agencies developing recreational facilities on reservoir margins." Thus, just as mediation can help settlement by focussing on the real rather litigable issues, it may also work in opposite fashion to allow divisive issues to remain unaddressed.

On the surface, the nature of the legal remedy would usually seem to favor the defendant, often a developer or a permit-granting agency. Eventual construction or the granting of a permit to commence construction may satisfy the defendant's desires. But legal delays cost money and delays can ruin long-range plans or obstruct a key phase of a large project. If the defendant were to lose his case, subsequently appeal the decision, and eventually be forced to abandon even a scaled-down (compromise) project, the impacts of delay could be substantial.

SOCIAL PSYCHOLOGY

Question 6: Will the personalities and positions of the chief negotiators have a major influence on the settlement?

Discussion: The experiences of Cormick and Fradin in their respective disputes suggest that choosing an able, dedicated negotiating team which will bargain in good faith and be able to justify a compromise settlement to its constituents improves the chances of an environmental mediation effort. Since environmental disputes involve emotional issues, the personalities and philosophical positions of the chief negotiators should be evaluated by the mediator. Will certain persons tend to be uncompromising over key issues? Is one negotiator so weak and uncertain of his position that he will be fearful of making commitments without approval, causing delay? Will negotiators be willing to continue, in the face of deadlines and stalemates, to work toward a settlement?

Once a settlement is reached, ability of negotiators to satisfy emotional needs of the groups they represent—to "sell" to their groups the settlement as realistic and desirable compromise—is of prime importance. Implementation can only occur if the parties are willing.

Implementation may be improved by an earlier face-saving function on the part of the mediator. During bargaining, the act of compromising on a key point could show an obvious retreat from the publicly stated position of one of the negotiators. After the settlement record becomes public, knowledge of this retreat may damage feelings to the extent that implementation is inhibited. The mediator can often avert such damaging losses of face.

Occupational constraints on the negotiators will also influence their bargaining actions. To review Cormick's 1977 classification of parties in attendance at public hearings, some groups are mandated to provide written comments on proposals; others voluntarily make oral or written statements for the record; others grant permits but have little discretionary authority; and, still others have enforcement authority coupled with a broad policy mandate and review powers. Above these, a federal agency may have a broad policy to promote and indirect means of enforcement.

The mediator can attempt to anticipate how each party will strike a posture, for effect or otherwise, because of these legal, administrative, or ideological constraints on the group or agency he represents. This analysis could also be used in the selection of appropriate parties to be represented at the negotiating table. In addition, the mediator should have in view those agencies that have the authority to review, veto, or modify a mediated settlement (see discussion under "Political Science" questions in this chapter).

Question 7: At what stage is the conflict? Does an impasse exist in the minds of the bargaining parties?

Discussion: The stage of conflict as it pertains to particular disputes has been discussed previously (see Chapter Four). Analysis of stage of conflict can be accomplished by constructing a detailed chronology, such as the one on Snoqualmie (Fig. 6, Chapter Five), conducting interviews, and reviewing the written record of the controversy.

Work in the Snoqualmie case has suggested to Cormick (1976: 3) that an impasse must be reached before mediation can occur. Even though Cormick's term "pre-negotiations stage" suggests an initial stage of conflict, it is actually a sub-stage of what might be termed the second phase of the dispute (Fig. 15). If we review Fig. 6, the period 1959-1973 showed initial flooding, public outcry, Corps studies and plans, public reviews, and public hearings—but no apparent chance for settlement. The parties reached an impasse. The second phase began when Cormick's pre-negotiations work (Stages 3 and 1a, Fig. 15) determined suitability for mediation, established credibility and trust with parties, and obtained endorsements from proper officials. Negotiations followed. The mediated settlement was ratified by the parties and is undergoing implementation.

Using conflict stage analysis, one can determine whether conditions are suitable for mediation. If there has been a record of controversy, notes Cormick, an impasse results in (1) well-defined issues, (2) visible and involved parties, (3) a sense of urgency, and (4) a dawning realization that none of those concerned can unilaterally achieve their objectives. The dispute is ripe for mediation.

The human side of conflict is important to the mediator. Through analysis of the persons involved, conflict emerges as an instrument of social integration and definition. The third party, serving as a catalyst for settlement, must make the social and psychological needs of the parties work in favor of good feeling and compromise.

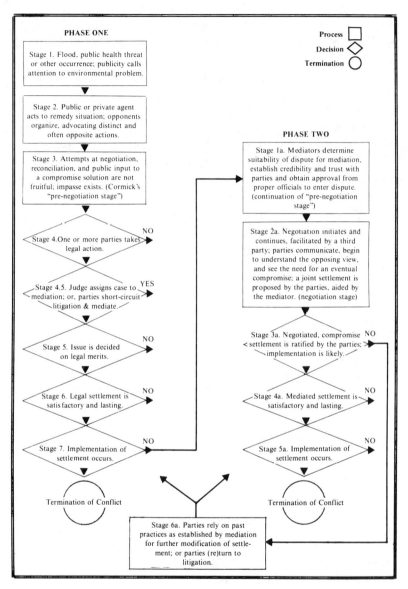

Fig. 15.   An operational model of stages in the environmental conflict situation. An operations format is used to show process, decision, and termination steps; of course, the process is not quantified and operates by the use of subjective judgments.

POLITICAL SCIENCE

Question 8: At what levels has political and administrative decisionmaking taken place regarding the conflict? Which decisions were most important? Has the arena of decisionmaking (and therefore the arena of conflict and settlement) changed over time? If so, how?

Discussion: After becoming familiar with the conflict record, the prospective mediator can use a simple diagram to analyze decisionmaking arenas pertaining to the dispute. Reserve Mining is an especially good example, embracing as it does local, state, regional, and national interests (Fig. 16). Through time, the arena of conflict enlarged from local and state hearings, permits, and media coverage to include regional and national input. Other states and federal agencies were represented in litigation. The federal government and adjoining states subsequently assumed advisory roles in the dispute, with the Minnesota Pollution Control Agency, Minnesota Environmental Quality Council, and Reserve as protagonists. The final arena of settlement will probably be the State of Minnesota.

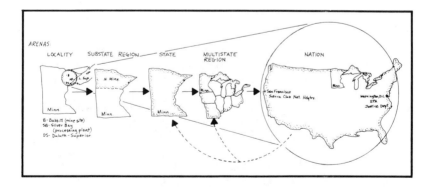

Fig. 16. (continued)

ARENA: Year	Local	Substate Region	State	Multistate Region	Nation
	("local concern")				
prior to 1947	*				
1947	*	*	*		
1955	*	*	*		
1956	*	*	*		
1958	*	*	*		
1959	*	*	*		
1967	*	*	*		
1968	*	*	*		
1969	*	*	*	*	*
1970	*	*	*	*	*
1971	*	*	*	*	*
1972	*	*	*	*	*
1973	*	*	*	*	*
1974	*	*	*	*	*
1976	*	*	*	*	

1959 * - date of documented involvement (study, impact hearing, conference, regulatory action, etc.) by this decision-making arena in Reserve Minining dispute.

Fig. 16. (continued)

The diagram shows the changes in decisionmaking arenas (and therefore arenas of conflict and settlement) over time in the Reserve Mining dispute. The diagram was prepared from political science and regulatory indicators. Similar analyses could be performed, perhaps with more difficulty, showing horizons of economic inter-dependence, media coverage, public trust, and concern mong scientists and technologists. Note the shift of focus back to state regulatory agencies and Reserve in 1976, which would suggest, along with the narrowing of issues and the recognition of a successful mediation effort in Moorhead, that the Reserve dispute was potentially more mediable at that time than at any time the previous seven years.

A similar example has been constructed by Wood (1976: 149) for a water resources controversy in British Columbia (Fig. 17). Wood charted the growth of involvement in this controversy by monitoring relevant press statements by officials at progressively higher levels of government. Over time, concern was shown (in ascending order) by community lead-

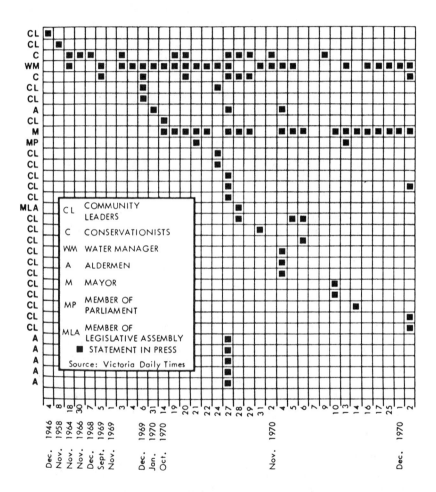

Fig. 17. **The growth of involvement in a water resources controversy in British Columbia as determined by press statements (after Wood, 1976).**

ers, conservationists, water managers, aldermen, the mayor, and a member of the legislative assembly. The arena of conflict became enlarged as the controversy gained significance. Analyses of changes in decisionmaking and concern levels over time can advise the mediator of the political implications of conflict and settlement.

Analysis of the decisionmaking processes and the arenas of conflict and settlement will also identify those who will implement a forthcoming settlement. Since the key to success of any settlement is implementation, identification of significant decisionmaking parties is essential.

Question 9: Does one decisionmaking body have the authority to make a final decision (e.g., issue a permit) or to review, modify, or veto a mediated settlement terminating an environmental dispute? Should this party be encouraged to participate as a member of a negotiation/mediation effort?

Discussion: The occupational constraints on negotiators, as discussed earlier, are functions of the agencies they represent. Cormick (1977) identified three or four levels of involvement among participants at public hearings (Chapter 3; and Question 6, this chapter).

The mediator must certainly reckon with the high-level enforcement and policy agencies. McCloskey (1977) has noted that:

> A complicating factor in resolving such environmental disputes is that most depend on the Government for the final decision. Thus, most of them are really three-cornered contests, with the Government not really acting as a mediator but as a superior third party with pretentions to wider knowledge and legitimacy than the other two parties.

The mediator must explore whether the Government, as McCloskey puts it, should become a party to the negotiations. In some cases, it will undoubtedly decline an invitation.

A further complication arises if the case goes to court after a mediation effort is completed. The judge may be required to decide whether a mediated settlement contract or memorandum of agreement has stature as evidence, and whether the review agency acted properly by participating in out-of-court negotiations. He may rule that the agency acted improperly and contracted away its administrative or statutory authority (Kurtz-Phelan, 1977); or he may decide that the agency had discretionary authority and exercised it properly.

In order to summarize and to adapt Cormick's observations to this discussion, the mediator might classify parties to a dispute in the following manner.

(1) An agent might have primarily *statutory obligations.* For example, if an agency *must* make a decision whether to grant or not grant a special conditional permit, it may not wish to participate in preliminary negotiations which would prejudice its final decision. Citizen commissions, whose staffs sometimes participate in preliminary negotiations, often find themselves in difficult positions when a final permit decision might be made.

(2) An agent might have primarily *discretionary authority.* For example, the Corps of Engineers has some latitude as to where its projects will be located, and takes into account the opinions of the proposed project state (see the Snoqualmie discussion). State parks departments exercise discretionary authority when locating a new facility. Municipalities have discretion in the location and configuration of industrial facilities within their jurisdiction.

(3) Finally, an agent might best perform the important function of providing *"good offices."* Governor Dan Evans of Washington provided this service and endorsement concerning the Snoqualmie dispute (see discussion following Question 10), and Congresswoman Pat Schroeder of Colorado began performing this function for the Foothills controversy (see Chapter Five).

Each of the classifications above, especially (2), appears to give the mediator a sorting mechanism for parties, and in turn disputes, that might be suitable for mediation.

Question 10: Specifically concerning the decisionmakers, has the state governor played an important role in the conflict?

If so, has he aided or hindered settlement? Would he favor the use of mediation techniques?

Discussion: As the state's chief executive, the governor of any state is highly visible. A look at the performance of several governors pertaining to environmental conflicts in their states will demonstrate the significance of the governor's actions to a mediation effort.

Governor Dan Evans of Washington, a former engineer, assumed a supportive but restrained posture in the Snoqualmie River dispute. Evans originally opposed the Corps plan for two dams on the river, but was not committed strongly either to a development or to a preservationist position. He officially endorsed the mediator's entrance into the dispute and their attempts to reconcile the parties, and then followed progress of the mediation effort with interest. Settlement, when it came eight months later, was endorsed by Evans as a manifestation of the democratic process.

Governor Patrick Lucey of Wisconsin, a former agribusiness manager and realtor, was initially for and later against the Kickapoo Dam. Lucey's changing positions, budget maneuuverings in Congress, and actions of Wisconsin's Congressional delegation all served to complicate the dispute and magnify its political nature. Mediation, although proposed to the governor, was apparently precluded by the advanced stage of conflict, Corps initiatives, and the tenuous financial status of the project. The apparent settlement, now undergoing implementation, is similar to the mediated outcome concerning Snoqualmie.

Governor Hugh Carey of New York was facing fiscal and environmental crises when forced to act in the Hudson River PCB case. Underlying Carey's publicized support for Conservation Commissioner Reid's policies and objectives was the fact of New York's difficult financial status. GE's offer of a "good faith" payment was probably acceptable to a majority of New York citizens, both as a fair compensation for what had been done free of charge by many industries in the past and as a means for keeping the plant in operation and securing jobs and incomes. But the relationship between Carey and Reid was reportedly strained due to past confrontations.

Reid's public statement that the payment was unacceptable and compromising to public health was, for obvious political reasons, not supported by Carey. Opposing statements by industry intervenors seemed to obstruct settlement by damages payment as had been proposed by out-of-court negotiations. Someone had to give, and Reid did, by resigning his position. Carey's actions and Reid's uncompromising stance intensified the conflict.

If the governor is actively involved in an environmental conflict, his activities should be scrutinized by the mediator. Were the governor's actions during the various stages of conflict politically expedient ones, or did they follow a consistent policy? Also, what is the governor's occupational background, and how might it influence his perspective on a particular dispute?

Because the governor is highly visible, his attention (e.g., by making statements to the press) to a particular environmental dispute heightens public perception of that dispute and can either help or hinder the mediation effort. If public opinion appears evenly divided, promotion of mediation by the chief executive may be constructive and politically expedient. The governor who adopts a hard-line, emotional position opposing or favoring a project is identified with that project. If the project culminates in a position opposite to that which the governor desires, a serious loss of face could result. It would seem that a promotion of settlement of most environmental disputes is a promotion of the highest public good for the citizens of a state, and that a governor would frequently do well to encourage mediation.

A comparison between the state's chief executive and the members of the state legislature and Congress is also instructive for the mediator. Because of his position, the governor is key to the success or failure of a project. Some actions of federal agencies suggest that their policy is not to push construction if the governor is in opposition (e.g., the Snoqualmie case). The governor can also block constituents' appeals to Congress by taking administrative action, such as directing a state agency head to handle the matter in a certain way. And because the governor is a single person in a single office with singular powers, his actions can be swift and decisive if he wishes them to be. This is in contrast to appeals to the state legislature for remedy—often a slow and tortuous process taking years to produce results because of the multitude of persons, interests, and procedures.

Question 11: What types of decisions may result from a mediated settlement? How will the decisions affect interest groups as parties to the dispute?

Discussion: The types of decisions produced by settlement of an environmental conflict have been discussed previously in the case studies. The work of Theodore Lowi (1964) has been used to categorize the types of decisions made regarding affected interest groups. To recount briefly, Lowi's categories (as we are adapting them to environmental decisions) are:

(1) *distributive* - decisions which confer public benefits, divisible among specific individuals, firms, groups, or localities, and which have no perceived public injury.

(2) *regulatory* - decisions which confer specific benefits on large identifiable parties and incur specific, perceived costs to other identifiable parties (e.g., railroad industry, Teamsters' Union).

(3) *redistributive* - decisions which have direct, society-wide impacts, deliberately benefitting and burdening large segments of the population (e.g., the middle class, all blue-collar workers).

Hart (1974: 127), in his discussion of Lowi's categories, asks if all decisions are gravitating toward redistributive significance. Re-examination of many of the case studies suggests that the question might be answered affirmatively. Environmental groups may try to attach society-wide significance to every fallen tree or dammed river, claiming that each action damages all society for current and future generations. Developers may see every regulation and every unfavorable legal opinion as damaging to future business. Both extreme positions are justified to some extent as economy/environment confrontations become more frequent and a philosophical difference is apparent.

Regarding mediation, it is suggested that those disputes which are confined to the distributive or lower-level regulatory category are best suited to compromise. It follows that confining the arena of conflict to a small geographic area (by controlling media coverage and preventing lawsuits with nationally-affiliated groups as intervenors, for instance) is an important function of the mediator. Cormick and Fradin limited the boundaries of their disputes successfully so as not to make resolution a large-scale regulatory or redistributive decision.

Lowi's categories may therefore be used in their adapted form to discover potential for mediation. A few words of caution: the categories were originally proposed for tariff-making policy, and therefore may not fit every environmental dispute. Likewise, there may be disagreement regarding the category into which a dispute fits. Lowi's categories simply give another appraisal of environmental disputes.

GEOGRAPHY

Question 12: In terms of geographic scale, how might one analyze the dispute under study concerning natural resources involved, inputs required for, and direct and indirect outputs (externalities) of, the resources development? Where are the points of conflict?

Discussion: The mediator could attempt to analyze environmental disputes as to relationship, distributions, and categories of natural and human resources. Fig. 18, as suggested by Question 12, attempts to describe the relevant geographic scales concerning resources development in the Reserve Mining dispute. Construction of the diagram shows that the natural resources involved are localized, but that, beginning with inputs for resources development, there are national and perhaps international implications for the remaining analysis levels. The cause/effect, mining/refining/distributing/residuals sequence is evident as one follows the diagram to direct and indirect outputs of development. It is then an easy matter to label sources of conflict and their geographic scales of relevance. The next step is a determination of which parties produce or

GEOGRAPHIC SCALE

	LOCAL-50 MI RADIUS (Silver Bay)	STATE (Minn.)	REGIONAL (Midwest) (Great Lakes) (Iron Range)	NATIONAL	INTER-NATIONAL
NATURAL RESOURCE(S) INVOLVED	iron ore deposits				
INPUTS FOR RESOURCE(S) DEVELOPMENT	workers ___ service functions _ transp. facilities etc.	___state ___ permits ___ and ___ licenses	water _____ transport- Great _____ Lakes mining mach- inery & equip.	water transport- Great Lakes & e. coast U.S. fed. per- mits & lic- enses	capital? (Republic & Armco are international corporations)
OUTPUTS OF RESOURCE(S) DEVELOPMENT	*tailings into L. Superior air pol- lutants taconite pellets jobs, etc.	*tailings & airborne pollutants taconite pellets jobs, etc.	tailings taconite pellets	taconite pellets for steel production	balance of payments
EXTERNALITIES (SPILLOVER EFFECTS)	*health hazard? fuel consump- tion mined land, etc.	*health hazard to n. coast of L. Superior? *need for on-land disposal site- arguments over econ. feasibility	*health hazard? Mich-Wis heightened perception of dispute industrial facilities siting precedent	*health hazard? nat. env. groups intervene effects on steel- related industries heightened perception	foreign view of U.S. business/ government/ environment relationship

*sources of conflict

Fig. 18.   An analysis by geographic scale of the environmental dispute involving the Reserve Mining Company in northern Minnesota.

regulate or experience which impacts. This determination helps the mediator decide who would implement a mediated settlement and how they would perform the implementation.

This scale of conflict analysis, can be extended by discussing another notion—the *arena of conflict*. This phrase has been used and discussed briefly several times in this chapter. The geographic section seems most appropriate for a complete explanation.

The arena of conflict for any environmental dispute can be characterized in several ways. Three characterizations are most pertinent, however.

(1) *Geographic Map.* Figures 16 and 18 depict mapped areas of geographic influence, conflict, and settlement. Geographic areas are delineated physically and politically, leading to use of conflict analyses such as those shown in the above figures.

(2) *Decision-making Forum.* The arena of conflict can be viewed as a Roman arena, with various parties (combatants) entering and leaving at different times as dictated by their interests. This arena may be an actual room or forum (e.g., a hearing room) or it may be a pervasive atmosphere of public statements, media coverage, and the give-and-take associated with any healthy public debate.

(3) *General Purpose Government.* Figure 16 suggests that various levels of general purpose government define the arenas of conflict. An arena shift will affect the chances for a mediated settlement, as previously discussed concerning Reserve Mining and a shift back to the State of Minnesota. It should be noted that southern Minnesota will never be directly affected by the Reserve decision; nevertheless, all Minnesota residents, including those from the southern part of the state, elect state officials who participate in state and federal agency decisions. Southern Minnesotans also furnish state and local decisionmakers, and comprise the voting public which holds all state decisionmakers accountable.

The three types of conflict arena show some relationship to Lowi's categories of distributive, regulatory, and redistributive decisions. Distributive and regulatory decisions obviously involve geographic areas whose residents receive benefits and pay costs. Even a large, commercial interest such as the railroad industry can be delimited geographically. Redistributive decisions are difficult to fit here, since the geographic areas, decision forums, and levels of government are often national in scope, including Congress, federal agencies, many diffuse interests, and sets of constituents throughout the country.

It might be said that mediability is enhanced when decision forums in each jurisdiction (local to intermediate to national, where appropriate) accept mediation, or when one forum sees that its decision will be preempted by another body according to legal or administrative rules. Once again, if all present and potential parties desire and are incorporated into negotiations, chances for a negotiated/mediated settlement increase.

Question 13: Have incorrect perceptions of time, space and distance added to the environmental conflict? Could a precise evaluation of affected geographic areas aid in settlement?

Discussion: The geographic content of environmental conflict is often significant to settlement. Location, locational decisionmaking, direction, distance, situation or relative location, distribution and its patterns, spatial variability, land use, and environmental perceptions are among those qualities that Browning (1974: 138-139) has designated for rendering a topic "geographical." All environmental disputes fit this designation with little difficulty.

The question, however, concerns misperceptions of the geographic content of environmental cases. Regarding New York State Public Service Commission decisions, Burggraf (1975) notes that "surely every case has involved some incorrect perceptions of environmental impact based on the inability to accurately assess the dimensions of installed facilities, e.g., transmission towers." He goes on to cite two cases in which misperceptions affected the outcome. In the first case, a court decision requiring the laying of transmission lines underground was reversed by the State Court of Appeals. The reversal may be interpreted as a rejection of the wording of the lower court decision since the precise geography intended to be affected by the order was difficult to determine. In the second case, uncertainty regarding precise boundaries of the Adirondack Preserves, state lands, and the Blue Line (limit of extension for provided utilities) have impelled re-hearing.

It is imperative for the mediator to recognize such mis-perceptions with reference to a conflict being considered for mediation. The communication/facilitation process is highly capable of insuring that each party has the proper and correct data, maps, and diagrams necessary for negotiations. But the many variables in environmental disputes combined with the complex wording of legal contracts may easily confuse dimen-sions or distances. The purpose of third party intervention is to clarify discrepancies so that productive dialogue may occur. To this end, Straus (1977) has suggested and researched the notion of "data mediation": using computers to help negoti-ators agree on, store and retrieve information in bundles the human brain can handle.

Question 14: What is the physical and cultural setting of the dispute? Would construction of a map, drawing, or dia-gram showing the environmental conflict setting (in a fairly complete but general fashion) be useful to the negotiators for purposes of seeing "the big picture"?

Discussion: The geographer's concern with resources and their distribution causes him to rely heavily on maps. A map may show any features, arrangements, or relationships that are relevant and needed for informational purposes by the negotiators. Again, the relationship to the geographic arena of conflict is apparent.

The map-picture showing the environmental dispute set-ting for Reserve Mining is suggested as a useful type of visual aid to negotiation (see Chapter Six, Fig. 6). Fig. 6 depicts elements of both the physical and human setting, showing distances, transportation modes, mining techniques, surround-ing population centers, production data, topography, vegeta-tion, water resources, natural pollutants, lake currents, and many other features. To accompany the map-picture, the mediator could assemble a fact sheet giving population and economic data, describing other relevant physical and human aspects of the landscape, and listing bibliographic references for further reading. He could also compile check lists of interest groups, issues, and value judgments; or he could assemble questionnaires which list the above, and poll members of the negotiating group (see discussion of dialectical scanning in Chapter Five). The map-picture, for instance, might appear quite different if different members of the negotiating group were asked to construct it. Such a technique might instruct the mediator regarding how the dispute is perceived geographically by various parties.

No map-picture, fact sheet, check list, or question naire can hope to address all facts and allegations pertaining to the dispute; but written and visual aids can serve to stimulate discussion and help the parties begin to understand opposing viewpoints The mediator must use caution as he prepares these materials, however, so that controversial or biased representations are not made which could damage his credibility with the parties.

If urging the negotiators to see "the big picture" is suggestive of the citizen participation/planning process, it is intended to be. And if Snoqualmie and Moorhead can serve as examples, the mediated settlement begins or adds to an incremental planning process for the particular region. The key difference from the citizen participation/planning process is, as Cormick emphasizes, that the mediated settlement must have a good chance of implementation, and must be negotiated with implementation in mind. The function described in this paragraph may also, with further refinement, provide a means for private environmental consulting firms to perform environmental mediation services as a planned, profitmaking activity. Indeed, Rivkin (1977) and Clark (1978) have both obtained consulting contracts to perform mediation services, as previously discussed in Chapter Five.

Question 15: What specifically are the resources involved in the dispute, and what redistribution of resources is expected or likely to occur upon settlement?

Discussion: The mediator can carry the parties' concerns with resources and their distribution further by suggesting joint evaluation of each resource relevant to the dispute. Koch and others (1960: 10-13) have suggested that resources have a positive or negative value in cases of international conflict. A resource might be described as positive if it provides natural defenses, strategic materials, food, or manpower. A negative resource could constitute a lack of strategic materials, an indefensible position, or food and manpower shortages. The state, inventorying its resources, considers its credits and liabilities before determining what it would like to acquire (its set of policy conditions) and the ranking or priority, of each of these policies. Similarly, parties to an environmental dispute and the mediator assessing a dispute might pinpoint the interactions among resources, their distribution, how they are perceived, and the means for achieving goals in particular jurisdictions.

Four geographic aspects of resources, as identified by Koch, are useful in local, intra- and interstate, national, and international environmental disputes. The four aspects are: (1) *form* in which the resources are to be found; (2) *arrangement* of the various resources with respect to each other; (3) *boundaries* of the natural resources; and (4) *instruments* for affecting change in the resource distribution. If the parties to environmental conflict view mediation as the instrument for change and subsequently order the geographic elements (resources), their perception of them (and their opponents' perceptions), and their priorities, the problem and the solution might become apparent. Perceptions of positive and negative values of resources and other, more abstract issues are perhaps the key to assessing which compromise will satisfy an opponent's desires while preserving the goals of one's own party.

Moreover, since resources distribution and redistribution are common to labor/management and community conflicts as well as environmental disputes, many negotiators will easily adapt to this type of analysis. In the end, environmental disputes come down to a change in resource distribution—the goal of mediation is a satisfactory accommodation for all parties.

Figure 19 summarizes some of the issues and events presented in the foregoing questions and suggests approaches for the mediator should these situations confront him.

It is evident from each of the questions presented here that analysis of environmental disputes for mediation, even from disciplinary perspectives, embodies an interdisciplinary approach. One cannot ask about effluent charges without considering the political outlook. Similarly, a discussion of the legal prospects for settlement must take in an analysis of the social and psychological composition of the opposing party. Such interdisciplinary considerations have provided the basis for the foregoing questions and discussions. What conclusions about environmental disputes and their mediability can be made? The final chapter addresses this question.

Potential Issue or Event	Suggested Approach For the Mediator
—Disputed B/C analysis	—Conduct joint analylsis with parties; arrive at agreed upon values for costs and benefits; agree upon what part of dispute involves B/C ratios
—Market related dispute involving commercial products	—Allow market decisions by consumers to resolve dispute; help to encourage such resolution through publicity, testimony before Congress, or other means
—Dispute at impasse, but negotiable, ancillary issues exist	—Encourage parties to consider side payments, penalties, or effluent charges which might promote compromise
—Favorable or unfavorable legal factors or history concerning the dispute	—Note past legal experiences and strength of the parties, history of litigation, conduct of judges, and related factors, and attempt to modify those which block mediation; define real issues, not just those litigable.
—Individual negotiators lacking sanction, reasonableness, or perseverance	—Attempt to have negotiators replaced, or to change conditions which cause individual problems
—Dispute at improper stage for negotiations to begin	—Wait until dispute is ripe for mediation, being careful not to promote conflict or heighten level of conflict artificially
—Inappropriate decision-making arenas for mediation effort	—Wait until arenas of conflict are suitable; if damaging stalemate exists, perhaps some action by sanctioned third party to change arena of conflict is justified
—Key party not participating in negotiations, e.g., government	—Encourage missing party to participate or at least endorse the mediation effort. Other types of participation could include observing or acting as a data resource.
—Governor in potential key role, but reluctant to act	—As above, attempt to persuade governor to endorse the mediation effort
—Incorrect perceptions of time, magnitude of impacts, or spatial relationships causing disagreement	—Correct situation through use of written and visual materials

Fig. 19.   Presented above is a summary table of a) potential issues and events that might confront the mediator, and b) suggested conduct for the mediator in the described circumstances. This table is intended to supplement the concluding summary table shown in Chapter Eight (Fig. 20). As with Fig. 20, this table gives general suggestions only, and may not universally apply to every type of category of dispute.

VIII.
Conclusions:
The Mediability of
Environmental Disputes

The conclusions presented in this chapter result from a survey of several dozen environmental conflicts over the four year period 1973-1977. Some of these conflicts were introduced in Chapter Six and analyzed in Chapter Seven. Others have been studied in depth but were not included as examples in Chapter Six. Still others were appraised on the basis of one or two written accounts or interviews, undertaken to gain perspective.

An intensive analysis of the two actual mediation efforts at Snoqualmie and Moorhead involved: an eighteen-month span of correspondence with Gerald Cormick concerning the Snoqualmie case; hearing Cormick's (taped) one-hour lecture on environmental mediation at the University of Minnesota, supplemented by discussion and comment by David Fradin (EBA mediator of the Moorhead dispute); an eight-hour discussion/interview with Fradin; a hearing of six hours of tapes on the Moorhead negotiation sessions; and, a review of information on each dispute supplied by Cormick and Fradin.

1. Geographic location and distribution of environmental conflicts—effects on mediability.

   Geographers, planners, and others have studied regional differences and the effects of those differences on economic development. The existence and arrangement of developable resources combined with geographic passages and barriers, soil and climatic types, demography, and other physical and cultural attributes help to determine future economic development of any given region.

   The nature, existence, and arrangement of resources help to determine the probabilities of and types of environmental conflicts in a region. At first glance, it would seem that environmental conflicts should be especially prevalent in those areas of the United States where a diversity of natural features exists. Combinations of natural features (scenic mountains, valleys, water, and wildlife) within one day's driving distance of large population centers should cause frequent conflicts over resource use. According to this reasoning, the relatively monotonous topography of the Great Plains of the United States would constitute a barren ground for environmental conflict. But such is not the case. The Great Plains have experienced, and will continue to experience, recurring conflicts resulting from major proposals for water resources developments by the U.S. Army Corps of Engineers and the U.S. Bureau of Reclamation. Even though almost every feasible location for water resources development on the Great Plains has been studied by federal agencies, problems will persist—floods and dam failures on certain river segments will create controversies, and power plant construction and reservation of natural areas (both usually contingent on water availability) will pit one interest against another.

   Similarly, those regions with hitherto unexploited wilderness, water, or scenic resources will experience conflicts pertaining to those resources, as different groups with different interests emerge from urban communication centers to contest resource use.

   Relative isolation of an area from the rest of the United States, such as is the circumstance for certain areas in Upper Michigan, northern Maine, and the Florida Keys, no longer guarantee unopposed development to alleviate local economic depression. Improved communications among environmental groups and growing public awareness of environmental impacts have created some opposition to every major effort at development. The Project Seafarer case exemplifies this circumstance. It follows that no region of the conterminous United States will be exempt from environmental conflicts in future years.

Every regional factor—existing and potential economic development, unexploited resources, and relative isolation—appears to influence the types of environmental conflicts which occur in a region. And regional factors also appear to influence mediability. The effective radius of major news sources is probably affected by physical and cultural barriers. Prominent newspapers with multistate circulation may inform many diverse groups of a potential conflict, hurting the chances for mediation by helping make the conflict too political and unwieldy and by causing it to have an inflated conflict arena. In many ways the print and electronic media help to determine the arena of conflict. By influencing the frequency and impact of the news for an individual or community, regional characteristics indirectly influence potential mediability.

Conclusions:

1A. **Regional characteristics, both physical and cultural, influence economic development, the numbers and types of intraregional environmental conflicts, and, indirectly, the mediability of those environmental conflicts in a particular area.**

1B. **Local and regional environmental conflicts concerning such issues as land use and zoning, water use and reuse, air quality, and industrial, commercial, residential, and recreational development will continue and will multiply throughout the United States in the forseeable future.**

1C. **Relative isolation of an area from the population centers of the United States no longer makes that area less susceptible to environmental conflict than more densely populated areas. The promise of economic benefits from development does not, as in past years, guarantee public acceptance. No region of the United**

States, the conterminous 48 states in particular, will be exempt from environmental disputes in the future, on whatever scale.

2. Mediability of environmental disputes in relation to size, location, and arenas of conflict.

As discussion in previous chapters suggests, the most readily mediable dispute appears to be one confined to a small geographic area. A conflict whose major impacts are limited to a portion of one state (a small river basin, for example) or to an area measuring 100-200 miles (160-320 km) on a side and including portions of no more than two states is manageable, and therefore amenable to out-of-court settlement. As the conflict grows to involve regional and national decisionmaking forums and larger than local general purpose governments, mediation is often precluded. Parties to the dispute may in fact desire a national hearing and prolonged discussion of the controversy. A national hearing may gain support for one particular position by generating publicity, forcing public statements by highly-placed officials, and focusing the issue in federal courts.

A conflict that has not been amenable to mediation may become so if the conflict arena is restricted. As a result, the dispute may become suitable for third-party intervention. A narrowing of the issues, a transfer of the regulatory arena from the federal government back to the state, or a call for out-of-court settlement by local and regional news editors could signal the mediator to begin pre-negotiations efforts. The Reserve Mining case evolved to such a stage of conflict.

However small, local conflicts may be of national importance. Settlement of local disputes pertaining, for instance, to energy resources and development, land use, and transportation can provide impetus for national policy. National environmental disputes might subsequently be reduced in intensity because of grassroots understanding of the issues.

The location and distribution of past environmental conflicts in a region may influence the potential mediability of a new conflict. Local and state forces may already be mobilized, accustomed to disputes of the type concerned, and prepared to take their case before the nation as another example of the economy/environment dilemma. Such circumstances may preclude mediation, but they also may set the stage for it if the need for the same energy or material resources happens to resurface later at another place. At such a resurfacing, parties may realize that a compromise is necessary, and work out their differences before a major controversy develops.

Conclusions:

2A. **The likelihood that negotiation/mediation procedures will settle a particular environmental dispute is greater if the arena of conflict is confined to: (1) a small geographic area (involving no more than portions of two states and an area 200 miles square); (2) manageable (local) decisionmaking forums; and (3) manageable (local) levels of general purpose government.**

2B. **Settlement by mediation of local environmental disputes has an impact on major, national environmental conflicts over resources. A potential major dispute might be settled informally because of grassroots support for a compromise position.**

2C. **The location and distribution of a developing environmental conflict relative to past conflicts may work for or against the mediator. By placing the dispute in perspective for local opposing interests, the mediator may effect compromise. Or, the cumulative effect of a long history of conflict in an area may be one of unresolvable polarization, especially when a new conflict further reinforces the polarization.**

3. Compromise and mediability of environmental disputes.

One of the prime goals of negotiation/mediation is to promote an atmosphere of cooperation, reasonableness, and understanding so as to aid the parties in fashioning a compromise solution. The mediator, in his passive role, can maintain a congenial atmosphere for bargaining. But how can the mediator, with no recognized power, suggest compromise solutions? As described here, the mediator is not playing the more active role of the fact-finder who reviews the arguments to the dispute, makes public his findings, and recommends various courses of action for settlement. The mediator can approach the problem in this way: *if the parties are not themselves pro-*

posing realistic compromises, the mediator may facilitate discovery by the parties of potential solutions to the conflict. A hint in a private caucus or a relevant piece of information could allow a negotiator to "discover" a good proposal and back it with personal conviction. The mediator must be an optimistic, encouraging observer, always confident of a chance for settlement.

Compromise may be thought of in the traditional sense as a scaling-down of one's demands in order to find an agreeable, middle position with another party. But environmental compromises are usually not clear-cut. Construction of a smaller facility or development of a smaller area may be a result of reasonable compromise; however, in some cases the choice is either no action or total action. Trading of negotiable, ancillary features of the disputed development may, in such cases, become realistic and appropriate during bargaining. Negotiation of location of support facilities, payment of compensation to local populations, and cooperation between developer and local officials in future environmental management functions are a few examples of ancillary aspects to the dispute that may be subject to compromise.

In summary, environmental mediators help opposing parties to see the need for compromise as a means of furthering society's progress. Extensive delays, although sometimes valuable for selected interests, usually cause social, economic, emotional, and ecological traumas that are undesirable.

Conclusions:
3A. One of the prime functions of the mediator is to convince opposing parties of the need for compromise. An atmosphere of reasonableness and good feeling must be promoted throughout the negotiating period.
3B. Negotiable, ancillary aspects of any dispute offer opportunities for compromise when it appears that either total action or no action are the best settlement choices. Compromise is necessary because extensive delays are usually destructive.

4. Parties to the dispute, their composition and relationships,

and the roles of party leaders and key officials in environmental dispute resolution.

An analysis of the parties to an environmental dispute should be an integral part of any pre-negotiations work performed by the mediator. Using the techniques, questions, and suggestions given in Chapter Seven, the mediator may come to understand the nature of each group, its relationship with other groups, and the goal it hopes to attain. Each conflict is unique, and group and individual behavior may not be predictable. Each conflict therefore requires a thorough analysis of party strength and composition with a view to eventual compromise.

The mediator should especially consider the institutional responsibilities and constraints on representative negotiators. Because of their employers, certain officials may be reluctant to comment, to make commitments, or to jeopardize future review responsibilities. Other officials may be required to comment, make recommendations, or promote policies in keeping with statutory or administrative responsibilities. Still other persons, often from advocate groups, may encourage technical and policy decisions which will further their interests and also influence the general public.

Regarding institutional responsibilities and constraints, the discussion and classification presented under Question 9 in Chapter Seven appears to provide a useful sorting mechanism for the mediator. Determination of which agents or agencies have primarily (1) *statutory obligations,* (2) *discretionary authority,* or which can provide (3) *good offices,* helps the mediator to classify parties, and in turn disputes, which might be mediable.

Of special importance among individual key officials who may be party to the dispute or who may provide "good offices" is the state governor.

The mediator might also attempt to locate other persons with pivotal roles in order to facilitate a settlement. To judge by the Moorhead and Snoqualmie experiences, there is no substitute for hard work and honest bargaining in environmental negotiations. Settlement may come sooner, however, if the mediator can arrange to expedite implementation with key officials.

Conclusions:

4A. An analysis of the parties to an environmental dispute, the arenas of conflict and settlement, and attendant geographic and political considerations should be included in any pre-negotiations work which the mediator performs. The mediator must be especially concerned about institutional responsibilities and constraints on each negotiator.

4B. Determination of which agents or agencies have primarily statutory obligations, discretionary authority, or can furnish "good offices" provides a useful sorting mechanism for the mediator as to mediable disputes.

4C. Special attention should be given to the role of the state governor and other key officials who might encourage mediation and expedite implementation of any mediated settlement.

5. Evaluation of the social and psychological interactions that take place between negotiating teams and individuals.

Interactions between individuals and groups in bargaining situations have been studied extensively by various disciplines. The behavior of negotiators in environmental bargaining situations is still speculative, however.

The interdisciplinary nature of environmental conflict is evident and thus the prospective mediator should have an inter-disciplinary background to analyze an environmental conflict and its parties. Several first-hand experiences with the principals are necessary before interpreting social and psychological indicators. Prediction is perhaps more speculative here than with any other element of the conflict setting.

Some behavioral factors do remain constant, however. The ranking of priorities in Chapter Two has been continually re-evaluated as this study has progressed. The final ranking (in descending order of importance) of what influences individual and group behavior remains essentially the same as that presented initially in Chapter Two:

(1) *economic self-interest,* the desire for personal financial gains;

(2) *social self-interest,* especially as it pertains to increased prestige and stature among peers (which in turn may lead to occupational advancement), political power, academic recognition, or recognition for humanitarian works;

(3) *personal value judgments,* such as feelings about growth, property rights, and use of technology; and finally,

(4) *concerns for natural systems,* and the impacts of alteration or destruction of natural systems on the earth and its inhabitants.

Conclusions:

5A. The social and psychological nature of the environmental bargaining situation is highly variable. Each dispute is unique and deserves further research and analysis to identify mediable aspects.

5B. The mediator can use the constant behavioral factors (in descending order of importance) of economic self-interest, social self-interest, personal value judgments, and concerns for natural systems to assess the individuals and groups as parties to environmental disputes.

6. Stage of conflict and the nature of future settlements.

The work of Cormick and Fradin and a study of the sequences of events in other environmental disputes suggest that mediation is most productive when a conflict reaches an impasse. For reasons already enumerated, an impasse puts the dispute in focus and creates an urgency that demands expeditious settlement.

The combination of stage of conflict and scale of the dispute may cause some environmental problems to solve themselves. If a dispute is in its initial, formative stage, the mediator may look to another, more suitable but indirect intervenor in our national environmental/economic system. Conflicts on a national scale could be resolved through the market. The controversy over use of aerosol propellants was resolved in the aforementioned fashion by a large and powerful force—the buying public.

Other, smaller conflicts may be mediated by a public official, concerned citizen, or a change in public use or consumption. The professional mediator can learn from the work of other, less-knowing third parties without actually participating himself. Disputes that need mediation are disputes that need facilitation, and those for which no proper facilitator exists.

We might say a further word about the nature of future settlements, especially settlements for those environmental controversies that are actively mediated. Developers carefully investigate many sites before they propose to manufacture, construct, transport, mine, or otherwise change the existing landscape. In their investigations the most controversial and obviously unsuited sites are rejected. The Snoqualmie and Moorhead settlements proposed development in some fashion in spite of strong initial opposition. Termination of the Kaiparowits power plant proposal is perhaps an exception to this trend but, as previously stated, Kaiparowits will surface under another name somewhere, sometime.

Will future settlements then tend to favor development interests? The answer is affirmative, but with an important qualification. The purpose of mediating environmental controversies is to cause something to happen, to resolve a problem. Development may proceed as a result of resolution—but it should be development that is controlled and yet progressive, environmentally responsible and yet job-creating, and an example of the enhancement of earth's resources by man. The goals are lofty ones. It will take much work, ingenuity and sacrifice to achieve them.

Conclusions:
6A. Mediation is most applicable to those environmental controversies which have reached a stage of impasse.

6B. Indirect and covert mediators may intervene to solve environmental conflicts in various stages at various scales. The professional mediator should recognize such mediators and analyze their work.

6C. Future, mediated environmental settlements will tend to favor development interests in the sense that some development will occur. One goal of mediation is to encourage responsible, planned, and progressive development that will preserve and enhance the natural and cultural environment of the earth.

To summarize the conclusions presented in this chapter, Fig. 20 shows suggested conditions of disputes appropriate for mediation and suggested methods and guidelines for a successful mediation effort. As the caption indicates, the suggestions are general in nature and will not universally apply to every type and category of dispute.

Mediation of environmental disputes will become a useful and worthwhile technique in our society. Indeed, this technique is presently being used in selected areas to solve environmental problems. The creation of a national clearinghouse to obtain research funds, train mediators, and generally promote the technique is further evidence of its validity. And, as an investigator, I have found it lonely, uncertain, and yet exciting to be on the frontier of a new idea. Through an exercise like this study one gains, in a small way, an appreciation of that feeling of anticipation, anxiety, and contribution peculiar to all innovators.

(A) Conditions of Disputes Appropriate for Mediation

—Favorable regional characteristics, both physical and cultural

—Shared interest in settlement,
without economic benefits as
overriding issue

—Manageable arena of conflict

—Available compromise solutions;
or, (if compromise solutions on
major issues are not reasonable)
negotiable, ancillary aspects of
the dispute which might help
promote settlement

—No major social/psychological

conflicts between individual
negotiators

—Ability of mediator to minimize
economic self-interest, social
self-interest, and personal value
judgments of negotiators

—Dispute has reached a stage of
impasse in which all sides will
generally "lose" by continuing
conflict

—Indirect and covert mediators
who assist in reaching a settlement

(B) Methods and Guidelines for a Successful Mediation Effort

—Stress overriding regional goals
of improving quality of life for
present and future residents;
promote shared interest in
settlement

—Confine arena of conflict, if
national intervenors (such as
CEQ) become involved, help to
make their input conciliatory
and use them to promote compromise, if possible

—Place dispute in perspective
relative to national goals, priorities, and experience if this
placement will lessen polarization

—Generally, promote compromise
on major issues or identify negotiable, ancillary aspects of the dispute

—Identify parties and their responsibilities and constraints,
especially those who have dis-

cretionary authority, statutory
responsibility, or those who can
provide "good offices"

—Analyze carefully the social/
psychological make-up of the
individual, interacting negotiators; keep in mind the constant
behavioral factors of (in descending order of importance) economic self-interest, social self-
interest, personal value judgments, and concern for natural
systems

—Use impasse situation to promote compromise

—Determine indirect mediators
and assist their efforts

—Encourage responsible, planned,
and progressive development;
educate all parties as to the costs
of unbalanced growth

Fig. 20. Presented above is a summary table of: (A) suggested conditions of disputes appropriate for mediation; and (B) suggested methods and guidelines for
a successful mediation effort. The table gives general
suggestions, which may not universally apply to
every type and category of dispute (see also Fig. 19,
Chapter Seven).

APPENDIX

Background Information Concerning Environmental Mediation

————————————————————————————— **Page 11** ——
**Excerpted from: Cormick, Gerald W. 1973. Environmental mediation: an
action proposal. Community Crisis Intervention Center,
Washington Univ., St. Louis, Mo., 29 November, 18 pp.**

REACTIONS FROM THOSE INVOLVED

Those with the broadest experience in the attempted resolution of
environmental conflicts though the courts are among the most eager to find
viable alternatives for at least some of the disputes in which they are involved.
In an effort to better understand the dynamics of environmental disputes and
ways in which the mediation process might be applied, the author of this
proposal has talked at length with environmentalists, industry and corporate
spokesmen, lawyers representing industry, environmental groups and public
agencies, government agency staffs and political decision-makers. Almost without exception there was an eagerness to explore the mediation process, both as
an alternative to litigation and as a means of avoiding the kinds of confrontation
which make litigation inevitable:

The Director of a public interest law firm mentioned a number of disputes—

Page 12

including freeway siting, the use of open space, and even advertising and its effect on
power consumption—where precedents have been established in the courts and
planners and decision-makers were now willing to develop plans which recognized
a broad spectrum of perspectives. From his point of view, the lack of an adequate
mechanism for joint decision-making with which to follow up on court victories had
lessened the impact of such precedents. He mentioned several specific disputes,
including one involving the future development of a major open-space area near a
large urban center, in which he felt the negotiation/mediation process could and
should be applied.

A senior regional official of a major federal department outlined a number of
situations where citizen participation had exacerbated a problem. While he felt such
participation was both necessary and desirable, the processes available only raised
issues and could not resolve them. It left him still in the position of making unilateral
decisions, only now there were more clear-cut "winners" and "losers". He feels that
mediation could both raise and resolve the important issues.

An attorney who has represented a number of environmental groups described two
situations where mediation not only could have found a mutually satisfying
accommodation but prevented schisms within the community that threaten to have

long-range negative effects. One was a dispute over the way in which privately owned seashore would be developed. The disputants included a major environmental group, a large developer, private landowners, and local government units. The other involved development of a large housing complex and the issues included both aesthetic factors and concerns over pollution and demands for limited city services.

Page 13

A representative of a major multi-national corporation outlines a dispute in which they sought to find an accommodation of a dispute over the plant-siting and resource-use policies. The corporation was desirous of finding some plan which would satisfy the concerns of the environmentalists, the economic needs of the area, and the technical realities of the corporations. In the absence of an available third party it created a panel of "impartial" scientists to recommend the "best" plan and course of action. Disputes between competing environmental organizations, along with the manner in which the panel was assembled, resulted in abandoning the entire project at great expense to all involved.

Officials in two states are searching for a way of resolving conflicts surrounding the development and construction of flood control facilities. Disputing parties include those who are victims of the flooding, environmental groups concerned with the maintenance of wild rivers, developers, local governments and the Corps of Engineers. The problem is to develop some consensus between and commitment from major spokesmen of the conflicting groups, in order to provide at least some relief for victims of the flooding while meeting the concerns for the environment while avoiding litigation which could delay any action indefinitely.

An official of major federal agency outlined a dispute in which the agency was being sued over development of safety standards. Its concern is that is has not found any way to communicate its own concerns and dilemmas—or share the concerns of the environmental groups—outside the court process.

DRAFT

Proposed legislation for an environmental mediation service in Massachusetts, May 22, 1974.

Whereas, the deferred operation of this act would tend to defeat its purpose which is to assist in the resolution of present and future environmental disputes of concern to all residents of the Commonwealth, therefore, it is hereby declared to be an emergency law, necessary for the immediate preservation of the public convenience.

Section 1. In order to encourage the order and efficient protection and management of the natural resources of the commonwealth, the secretary of the Executive Office of Environmental Affairs is hereby authorized and directed to establish a voluntary environmental mediation service for the purpose of expediting the resolution of environmental disputes. Environmental disputes shall include, but not be limited to, issues concerning air pollution, water pollution, improper sewage disposal, pesticide pollution, excessive noise, improper operation of dumping grounds, impairment and eutrophication of rivers, streams, flood plains, lakes, ponds, or other surface or subsurface water resources; destruction of seashores, dunes, marine resources, wetlands, open spaces, natural areas, parks, or historic districts or sites. The environmental mediation service shall be available to help resolve disputes between private parties, including private corporations, disputes involving private parties and public agencies, and disputes among public agencies. Neither the establishment of such a service nor the mediation of any individual shall dispute increase or diminish the powers and duties of the secretary or any agency involved in such dispute nor shall participation in the mediation of any dispute relieve any agency of any existing but to permit or seek public comment or participation. No environmental mediator shall be empowered to settle disputes by arbitration unless the parties involved have executed written agreements to this end.

Section 2. In order to carry out the purposes of this act, the secretary of environmental affairs is hereby authorized to:

(a) appoint and remove environmental mediators without regard to the provisions of chapter thirty-one;

(b) accept or reject applications for mediation services;

(c) approve the assignment of personnel for periods of not more than thirty days from any agency within the executive office of environmental affairs to provide technical assistance, such assignments to be without prejudice to the employee's normal personnel or budgetary status;

(d) expend without prior appropriation any fees, charges, grants, or other funds received by the state treasurer from any public or private source for the purposes of this act;

(e) expend any state funds appropriated for the purposes of this act;

(f) enter into contracts with agencies or persons for technical or advisory services;

(g) develop and conduct training sessions and other appropriate information and education services relating to environmental mediation.

Section 3. Within sixty days of the effective date of the act, the secretary shall, without regard to the provisions of chapter thirty A of the general laws, establish rules and regulations governing the operation of the environmental mediation service which shall include specific guidelines describing the manner by which disputes may be accepted for mediation, the qualifications required of environmental mediators, the methods of conducting mediation sessions, the allocation of mediation costs and such other provisions as he may deem necessary.

Section 4. Within thirty days of the termination of any mediation case, the secretary shall cause to be published notice of the disposition of the dispute, and the written report of such disposition whall thereupon become a public document, provided, however, that the contents of such report shall be limited to a factual description of the dispute and an explanation of the method of termination of the mediation process. At least annually, the secretary shall file with the Governor and the General Court a complete account of environmental mediation activities conducted during the previous year, and such report shall also be a public document.

MEMORANDUM AGREEMENT

WHEREAS, the cities of Seattle, Mercer Island and Bellevue; the Municipality of Metropolitan Seattle (hereinafter "Metro"); and King County by and through their respective councils and the Washington State Highway Commission (hereinafter "the Commission") desire to resolve the disputes which have surrounded the plans to construct an improved Interstate 90 (I-90) facility between Interstate 405 (I-405) and Interstate 5 (I-5); and

WHEREAS, there is a desire to create an environment of cooperation in which agreement is reached among all parties concerned relative to the design of the I-90 facility and related transportation projects; and

WHEREAS, the decisions of the Ninth Circuit Court of Appeals of the United States District Court for the Western District of Washington have required that all alternatives to the proposed highway be studied; and

WHEREAS, all parties hereto state that they have reviewed the proposed highway development and all currently available alternatives to it, including the option of withdrawal and substitution; and

WHEREAS, the I-90 facility from I-405 to I-5, when constructed, must contain all of the social and environmental amenities included in the Commission's previously adopted plans and modifications thereof contained in the Findings and Order of the Board of Review in order to be acceptable to all jurisdictions; and

WHEREAS, the parties believe that construction of the agreed upon I-90 facility will be of definite advantage to all four local jurisdictions because it will provide an excellent transit way between Seattle, Mercer Island and Bellevue; it will eliminate the dangerous three-one reversible lane operation presently employed in that corridor; it will provide improved truck access from the east to Seattle's south industrial/commercial area and port; it will provide improved capacity in the off-peak direction; it will probably provide an improved facility sooner than other approaches; it will provide access to and from I-90 and I-5 south of downtown Seattle eliminating traffic presently going through Beacon Hill residential areas; it will provide many jobs for our citizens during the period of construction; and it will repair the corridor and help knit together the communities now split by U.S. 10 west of the Mount Baker ridge and across Mercer Island; and

WHEREAS, the parties have concluded that withdrawal and substitution is not a desirable option because it would double the local matching monies required and because Mercer Island and Seattle find unacceptable a major highway/transit I-90 facility without extensive environmental amenities which amenities might not be funded under the withdrawal and substitution alternative; and

WHEREAS, it is in the best interest of the citizens of the Puget Sound area and the State of Washington that this segment of I-90 be completed in an expeditious manner; and

WHEREAS, all jurisdictions believe that sufficient public hearings have been held on the project and that no further hearings should be held unless legally required; and

WHEREAS, the parties desire to identify and establish a reasonable assurance of construction of certain priority public transportation facilities which are contained in the 1990 Transportation System Plan for the Central Puget Sound Region and which serve to ensure that I-90 functions as an integral part of the region's transportation system; and

WHEREAS, the parties desire to ensure that these future improvements are consistent with the goals and policies for regional development presently under consideration by the Puget Sound Council of Governments (hereinafter "PSCOG") and the subsequent subregional land use element of the Regional Development Plan for the Central Puget Sound Region;

NOW THEREFORE, in consideration of the mutual and reciprocal benefits accruing to each of the parties hereto, it is hereby agreed as follows:

1. The Cities of Seattle, Mercer Island and Bellevue; King County; Metro and the Commission support the construction of a facility which will accommodate no more than eight motor vehicle lanes which are arranged in the following general manner:

   (a) Three general-purpose motor-vehicle lanes in each direction shall be constructed between the South Bellevue Interchange and I-5. In addition, there will be provision for necessary weaving lanes and possible local access across the East Channel, to be determined in accordance with paragraph 1(e) below.

   (b) The facility shall also contain provision for two lanes designed for and permanently committed to transit use. The eastern and western termini for these lanes shall be designed to facilitate uninterrupted transit and carpool access to downtown Seattle and to downtown Bellevue in accordance with paragraph 3 hereinbelow. The design shall be such as to accommodate the operation of the two transit lanes in either a reversible or in a two-way directional mode.

   (c) The facility shall be designed in a manner which, as much as practicable, minimizes the width of the roadway and the taking of land.

   (d) To the extent practical, the facility shall provide priority by-pass access for local transit to the general purpose motor-vehicle lanes.

   (e) The parties agree that the transit lanes shall operate initially in a two-way directional mode, at no less than 45 mph average speed, with the first priority to transit, the second to carpools, and the third to Mercer Island traffic. In the direction of minor flow, the transit lane shall be restricted to busses. The parties further agree that the initial operation of the East Channel bridge shall consist of only three general purpose auto lanes in each direction in addition to the transit lanes. In addition, there will be an acceleration lane from the South Bellevue Interchange which will terminate prior to the exit ramp at the East Mercer Interchange. The subsequent mode of operation of the facility shall be based upon existing needs as determined by the Commission in consultation with the affected jurisdictions, pursuant to paragraph 14 of this agreement. That determination will consider efficient transit flow, equitable access for Mercer Island and Bellevue traffic, and traffic-related impacts on Seattle.

2. The I-90 facility shall be designed and constructed so that conversion of all or part of the transit roadway to fixed guideway is possible.

3. The parties recognize that the planning, design and construction of efficient access at the eastern terminus and western terminus of this facility will enhance the operation of I-90 as a regional transportation facility. Therefore, the Commission, jointly with Seattle, Mercer Island, Bellevue, King County, and Metro, as their respective interests and responsibilities may dictate, shall immediately upon execution of this agreement undertake the development of the necessary plans and designs for, and shall further proceed, with the required public hearings and the preparation of the necessary environmental impact statements in order to obtain maximum eligibility for Federal Interstate funding for the construction of the following projects:

(a) Transit access from I-90 to downtown Seattle:

(b) Transit access from I-90 to I-405 and to the Bellevue central business district;

(c) Transit and general-purpose access from I-90 to the King County Stadium area; and

(d) Transit and general-purpose access from I-90 to arterials serving the north Duwamish industrial/commercial area and the Seattle waterfront;

(e) Transit access from I-90 transit lanes to I-5;

For any of the above projects or portions thereof which are not eligible for Federal Interstate funding, the Cities, the County and Metro with full support of the Commission, shall seek any available funding for such projects and shall make reasonable effort to complete the construction thereof prior to the completion of I-90.

4. The parties further agree, except as otherwise provided in this agreement, that the modified design of the facility will preserve and incorporate all of the provisions for community amenities and for reducing adverse environmental impacts as contained in limited access plans adopted by the State Highway Commission for

(a) the segment of I-90 from the West Shore of Mercer Island to the East Channel Bridge and for

(b) the segment from I-5 to the West Shore of Mercer Island (modified by the Findings and Order of the Board of Review dated March 26, 1973, and the Stipulation to Resolve Certain Issues incorporated therein, including but not limited to the provisions for a full lid tying affected Seattle neighborhoods together.

The lid shall be constructed to permit park and/or two-story residential or business construction (not industrial uses) to take place on top of the highway between the Mt. Baker tunnel and 23rd Avenue South. Additional loads may be acceptable following specific agreement between the Commission and the City of Seattle. The Commission agrees to fund the landscaping of the lid and the maintenance thereof except as may be agreed to by other parties.

5. The parties agree that the design of the entire facility shall include the following additional features:

   (a) a transit station permitting transfer of transit passengers at Empire Way South or 23rd Avenue South as more particularly set forth in the Findings and Order of the Board of Review.

   (b) a direct Highway connection for Rainier Valley to and from the east.

   (c) the Commission's plan for preserving access between Seattle communities over adjacent local city streets shall include improvements of South Norman Street between 20th Avenue South and 23rd Avenue South to provide access to the Judkins neighborhood, this being done in lieu of the development of South Judkins Street as provided in the Commission's adopted plan as modified by the Findings and Order of the Board of Review.

   (d) a continuous park/pedestrian link between Judkins Park and the lid over I-90 west of the Mt. Baker Ridge Tunnel.

6. The Commission agrees to participate jointly with the City of Seattle in an I-90 corridor area planning study for the purpose of designing alternative means of redeveloping areas adjacent to the I-90 project in Seattle. The extent of such study shall be defined and agreed to by Seattle and the Commission, and to the extent that the study relates to the effects of the I-90 facility in the corridor, it shall be funded by the Commission.

7. At the option of the local jurisdictions to be exercised within a reasonable time, the Commission shall transfer to the appropriate jurisdiction fee title of all state-purchased lands acquired for the I-90 project but which are outside the finally determined right-of-way lines of I-90 to the fullest extent and at the lowest cost legally possible.

8. The parties hereto agree that they will proceed under established legal processes, including regional transportation planning procedures of PSCOG and consistent with the approved Regional Development Plan of PSCOG, to determine those projects which are of highest priority in the Transportation System Plan and the Transportation Improvement Program as the Plan and Program apply to the King County subregion. The parties hereby agree that projects (a) through (g) listed below are of highest priority and shall so indicate in the process of establishing the King County Subregional Transportation Improvement Program, the Regional 1990 Transportation System Plan, and Metro's Comprehensive Public Transportation Plan. The Commission and Metro shall work with the local jurisdictions in undertaking location and design studies for these projects at the

earliest possible date commensurate with state, regional, metropolitan and local planning and priority programming practices. Projects to be considered through these processes shall include, but not be limited to, the following regional components of PSCOG 1990 Transportation Plan:

   (a)   Transit/carpool lanes and/or Surveillance Control and Driver Information Systems (SC&DI) on I-5 from I-405 at Tukwila to the King County Snohomish County line:

   (b)   The park-and-ride lots and flyer stops contained in the approved 1980 Plan as may be modified by Metro:

   (c)   Provision for a busway or exclusive transit/carpool lane(s) as a part of the SR 99 and SR 509 corridor including a crossing of the First Avenue South Bridge, consistent with Metro's transition planning for this corridor;

   (d)   Provision for a busway or exclusive transit/carpool lane(s) and/or SC&DI as a part of SR 520 from I-5 to I-405;

   (e)   Redesign, in a manner acceptable to the City of Seattle, of the lanes where SR 520 meets I-5 and at the Mercer Street egress from I-5 in order to improve transit flow and reduce the congestion on I-5 between Mercer Street and Roanoke Street;

   (f)   Provision for a busway or exclusive transit/carpool lane(s) and/or SC&DI as a part of I-405 from Bothell to Renton

   (g)   Provision for exclusive transit lane(s) on I-405 through Bellevue which shall also include provision for a freeway flyer stop and a park-and-ride facility on I-405 between Main Street and N.E. 8th in Bellevue and provision for I-405 access improvements to the Bellevue central business district as determined by the Joint State Legislative/Highway Commission and City of Bellevue I-405 Access Study.

9.   The parties agree that the I-90 facility should be operated in such a manner as to encourage growth and development in the presently urbanized areas of King County rather than in undeveloped areas. Therefore, the Commission shall conduct a study in coordination with the parties to this agreement to determine the feasibility and means of metering and controlling local access to I-90 east of Bellevue during peak hours.

10.   Seattle, Bellevue, Mercer Island, King County and Metro agree that dedicated public transit rights-of-way through downtown Seattle and through downtown Bellevue are compatible with the public transportation plans of this area and are desirable to be implemented in conjunction with the completion of the I-90 facility.

11.   Immediately upon the issuance of the environmental impact statement, another review team comprised of representatives chosen by each of the parties to this agreement shall be established to further monitor and advise the Commission on the development of the design and the implementation of the entire I-90 facility and the I-90 transit access provisions listed in paragraph 3 above. In addition,

review teams including elected officials and citizens from Seattle, Bellevue, Mercer Island and King County may be established to further monitor and advise the Commission upon the implementation and design of the I-90 facility.

12. Upon execution of this agreement, the Commission becomes responsible for the design and construction of the facilities described in this agreement that can be funded wilth federal interstate funds as well as any other facilities referred to in this agreement for which the Commission, by law, has the sole responsibility; and the several parties to this agreement become responsible for the design and construction of the remaining facilities referred to in this agreement; provided that all such undertakings are subject to available funding and legal and procedural requirements. Seattle, Bellevue, Mercer Island, King County and the Commission agree to process any permits required for construction of the agreed upon facilities in a timely and expeditious manner, as provided by law.

13. It is expressly understood that agreement to the above by the Commission is tentatively pending review of (1) the final environmental impact statement to be filed in connection with the project and (2) the hearing record being prepared in connection with the corridor-design hearing held in January and February 1976. It is also understood that the parties have reached this agreement under the assumption and on the condition that the funding for the project, in accordance with the modified design of said project as referred to in paragraphs 1, 2 and 4 and those eligible portions under paragraph 3 which will qualify for Federal Aid Interstate monies, is approved prior to the initiation of construction and shall be funded from federal and state funds, except as agreed to by the affected jurisdiction(s).

14. This agreement represents substantial accommodations by the parties of positions held heretofore. Such accommodations were made in order to achieve a unanimous agreement upon which to proceed with the design and construction of I-90 and related projects. This agreement, therefore, sets forth the express intent of the existing governing bodies that the parties to this agreement understand that their respective governing bodies are limited in the degree to which they can bind their successors with respect to the exercise of governmental powers vested in those governing bodies by law. Accordingly, the Commission will take no action which would result in a major change in either the operation or the capacity of the I-90 facility without prior consultation with and involvement of the other parties to this agreement, with the intent that concurrence of the parties be a prerequisite to Commission action to the greatest extent possible under law.

Dated this 21st day of December, 1976

COUNTY OF KING

By: __John G. Spellman_____
             (signature)

MUNICIPALITY OF METROPOLITAN
SEATTLE

By: ___C. Carey Donworth_____
             (signature)

WASHINGTON STATE HIGHWAY
   COMMISSION

By: ___W. A. Burley_____
             (signature)

CITY OF SEATTLE

By: ___Wes Uhlman_____
             (signature)

CITY OF MERCER ISLAND

By: ___Benjamin J. Werner_____
             (signature)

CITY OF BELLEVUE

By: ___M. F. Vanick_____
             (signature)

STATE OF MINNESOTA

COUNTY OF RAMSEY

DISTRICT COURT

SECOND JUDICIAL DISTRICT

Minnesota Public Interest
Research Group,

Petitioner

vs.

Minnesota Environmental
Quality Council,

Respondent.

Court File No. 410303

STIPULATION

Whereas Anheuser-Busch, Inc., a Missouri Corporation (hereinafter: Anheuser-Busch) proposes to construct a malting facility within the corporate limits of the city of Moorhead and

whereas the city government of Moorhead (hereinafter: City) wishes the malting facility proposed by Anheuser-Busch to be constructed within the city of Moorhead and has approved draft agreements to provide Anheuser-Busch, Inc. with water, sewer, and electric service and submitted an environmental assessment on the proposed facility to the respondent Minnesota Environmental Quality Council (hereinafter: MEQC) pursuant to regulations adopted by MEQC and

whereas respondent MEQC concluded that no environmental impact statement was required under the provisions of Minnesota Statutes Section 116D.04 and

whereas petitioner Minnesota Public Interest Research Group (hereinafter: MPIRG) has filed the petition in this case for judicial review of the decision of MEQC not to require an impact statement on the proposed malting facility and

whereas Anheuser-Busch has appeared in response to MPIRG's petition and City has filed petition for leave to intervene

Therefore, the parties MPIRG, City and Anheuser-Busch enter into the following stipulation and agreement:

1. Attached hereto and incorporated by reference are the draft agreements between City and Anheuser-Busch for water service (Exhibit 1), electrical service (Exhibit 2), and sewer service (Exhibit 3). These contracts which have been approved by the negotiators for the City and Anheuser-Busch contain the following amendments and delegations made during the course of negotiations in this action.

    (a) In section 3.2 of Exhibit 1 the following language was inserted:
    "Company agrees to implement the best technology economically available, consistent with quality of output, to reduce its water requirements."

    (b) The following sentences were deleted from Section 8.3 of of Exhibit 1:

"In the event of a service curtailment by City necessitated under the terms of this section, it is specifically agreed that City will curtail all non-essential water usages, such as lawn sprinkling and residential car washing, before reducing service to Company. It is further agreed that all industrial users will be curtailed in proportion to their normal usage, subject to rules and regulations and By-Laws of the Public Service Commission."

(c)   In section 3.3 of Exhibit 1 the following sentence was deleted:

"In such event, Company agrees to give substantial notice to City of its plan to expand plant capacity and City agrees to put forth its best efforts to accommodate Company in such increased requirements."

and replaced with the following sentence:

"In such event, Company agrees to give substantial notice to City of its plan to expand plant capacity and City agrees to duly consider Company's request for increased supply."

A similar deletion and addition was made to Section 2.1 of Exhibit 3.

Anheuser-Busch and City have agreed to these changes which in the opinion of MPIRG mitigate the immediate environmental impact of the proposed facility. Anheuser-Busch and City agree not to make any further addition, deletions or amendments to Exhibits 1, 2, and 3 which would nullify or reduce the effect of the changes denoted above.

2.   The facility proposed by Anheuser-Busch will have the capacity to produce approximately 6.4 million bushels of malt per year in its initial phase. Anheuser-Busch has designed expansion of this facility to a capacity of 12.8 million bushels per year. Anheuser-Busch and City acknowledge that under current regulations of MEQC, an enivornmental assessment must be prepared and submitted so that MEQC or its delegate may rule on the necessity for an environmental impact statement. Since the purpose of the impact statement and assessment is to allow for informed decision-making in matters which affect the environment, the City and Anheuser-Busch acknowledge that all environmental reports which are submitted under the Minnesota Environmental Policy Act and regulations pro-mulgated thereunder must be submitted in sufficient time so that an informed decision can be made without the threat of delaying the project. The City and Anheuser-Busch will voluntarily submit an environmental assessment if one is required.

3.   City, Anheuser-Busch and MPIRG agree that public information and participation are the essence of good government and central to environmental protection. To promote public understanding of all aspects of the proposed malting facility those parties agree that all documents filed by City with MEQC and all reports and letters exchanged between the parties to this action which deal with the effects of the proposed malting facility on the City of Moorhead and its citizens, both environmental and economic, should be available to the

public. City agrees to place copies of all these reports and documents at the public library and MPIRG agrees to make copies available for inspection at the office of its local board at Moorhead State University. The City agrees to transmit copies of all such reports to anyone who requests them, at no cost if possible, and for no more than the cost of reproduction, in any case.

4. The parties all recognize the need for a regional water resources management plan for the Moorhead region. MEQC, at its January 23, 1976, meeting passed the following resolution:

> THAT the Environmental Quality Council supports present plans of Moorhead to make a regional comprehensive management plan for the wisest use and allocation of the water resources; and
>
> THAT the Environmental Quality Council urges that such plan be done as a priority.

Such a plan will involve a description of the water resources of the region, a list of all users of water and their projected long-term water needs and the formulation of a plan for allocation and use of available resources among projected users.

City agrees to seek any state or federal funding which is available for preparation of such a plan. The appropriate area which a plan must cover appears to be Clay County, Minnesota and City agrees to seek the co-operation of Clay county authorities and to co-operate with them in the preparation of a plan.

Anheuser-Busch acknowledges that it expects to be the largest single user of water in Clay county. Anheuser-Busch along with other large industrial users of water have a particular interest in long range water planning. Therefore, Anheuser-Busch agrees that, to the extent that federal and state funds are not sufficient for this project or are available for only parts of the plan or on a matching basis with other sources of funding, it will contribute the funds necessary for such a plan, provided that the amount of the contribution to be made by Anheuser-Busch pursuant to this stipulation shall not exceed $25,000.

The parties agree that such a plan should be completed as soon as practicable and that it should be completed by October 1, 1978, the time when Anheuser-Busch intends to begin operation of its malting facility.

City agrees to take such steps as are reasonably necessary to complete such a plan by October 1, 1978, and to participate if necessary in the funding of such a plan with Anheuser-Busch and other large industrial users of water in the planning area.

In consideration of the foregoing, MPIRG, Anheuser-Busch and City agree that the within action should be dismissed with prejudice. Each party shall bear its own costs herein.

Dated May 14, 1976

Michael Milgrom
_____
                          (signature)
Attorney for Minnesota Public
  Interest Research Group

W. Charles Lantz
_____
                          (signature)
Dorsey, Marquart, Windhorst,
  West & Halladay
Attorneys for Anheuser-Busch, Inc.

STATE OF MINNESOTA   DISTRICT COURT

COUNTY OF RAMSEY   SECOND JUDICIAL DISTRICT

Minnesota Public Interest
Research Group,

                              Petitioner,

                                        ORDER FOR DISMISSAL
                                        WITH PREJUDICE.

              vs.

Minnesota Environmental
Quality Council,

                              Respondent,

                  vs.

Anheuser-Busch, Inc., a
Missouri Corporation, and
The City of Moorhead, a
Municipal Corporation,

                              Interveners.

The above entitled matter came on for hearing before the Court at a Special
Term thereof in the Courthouse in the City of Saint Paul, County of Ramsey,
State of Minnesota, on the 14th day of May, 1976. The Petitioner, Minnesota
Public Interest Research Group, appeared by and through their counsel,
Michael Milgrom; Respondent, Minnesota Environmental Quality Council
appeared by and through the Attorney General for the State of Minnesota
through his Assistant, Don Kannas; Intervener, Anheuser-Busch, Inc.,
appeared by and through its attorneys, Dorsey, Marquart, Windhorst, West &
Halladay and its counsel, Owen Kelley; Intervener, City of Moorhead,
appeared by and through its City Attorney, Robert J. Schaefer.

The parties having presented to the Court a Stipulation for Dismissal with
Prejudice, and having made oral arguments in connection therewith, and the
Court having examined all of the files and records of the instant action, and
further upon Motion of the attorneys represented, the Court did make the following Order:

IT IS HEREBY ORDERED, That the Stipulation for Dismissal with
Prejudice herewith filed by the parties is in all things approved and the within
and foregoing action is hereby fully dismissed with prejudice and without costs
to either party.

BY THE COURT: Dated this 14th day of May, 1976.

THE HONORABLE JEROME PLUNKETT
Judge of District Court

STATE OF MINNESOTA   DISTRICT COURT

COUNTY OF RAMSEY   SECOND JUDICIAL DISTRICT

Minnesota Public Interest
Research Group,

Petitioner

vs.

Minnesota Environmental
Quality Council,

Respondent

Court File No. 410303

STIPULATION FOR DISMISSAL

The parties to the above entitled action, Minnesota Public Interest Research Group and Minnesota Environmental Quality Council, along with Anheuser-Busch, Inc. which filed a notice of appearance herein, and City of Moorhead which has filed a petition for leave to intervene herein, agree and stipulate that the above entitled action shall be dismissed with prejudice. Each party shall bear its own costs herein.

Dated: May 14, 1976

Michael Milgrom	Don Kannas
(signature)	(signature)
Attorney for Minnesota Public Interest Research Group	Attorney for Minnesota Environmental Quality Council

D. H. Kannas	Robert Schaefer
	(signature)
Attorney for Minnesota Environmental Quality Council	Attorney for City of Moorhead

W. Charles Lantz

(signature)

Dorsey, Marquart, Windhorst,
    West & Halladay
Attorneys for Anheuser-Busch, Inc.

BEFORE THE
STATE OF WISCONSIN
DIVISION OF NATURAL RESOURCES HEARINGS

In the Matter of the Proposed Solid
Waste Disposal Facility by the City
of Eau Claire Located in the Town of
Seymour, Eau Claire County, Wisconsin

EX-78-49

FINDINGS OF FACT, CONCLUSIONS OF LAW AND CONSENT ORDER

On March 24, 1978 the Town of Seymour petitioned the Department of Natural Resourcces for a public hearing under sec. 227.075, Stats., to review the Department's decision not to prepare an Environmental Impact Statement (EIS) regarding the proposed "Seven Mile Creek" solid waste disposal facility of the City of Eau Claire located in the Town of Seymour, Eau Claire County, Wisconsin.

Formal prehearing conferences were held in Madison, Wisconsin on April 18, June 27 and August 9, 1978. On April 19, 1978 a notice of hearing was issued which stated that any person who wished to intervene in the proceeding must do so in writing to the presiding hearing examiner by May 3, 1978. The following persons were identified as the parties of record to this action:

Town of Seymour, by

>   Raymond C. Johnson, Attorney
>   415 South Farwell Street
>   Eau Claire, Wisconsin 54701

City of Eau Claire, by

>   Ted Fischer, City Attorney
>   City Hall
>   Eau Claire, Wisconsin 54701

Thomas J. Dawson, Public Intervenor
Department of Justice
123 West Washington Avenue
Madison, Wisconsin 53702

Department of Natural Resources
Divisions of Enforcement and Environmental Standards by

>   Peter D. Flaherty
>   P.O. Box 7921
>   Madison, Wisconsin 53707

Maryann Calef, Assistant Attorney General
114 East, State Capitol
Madison, Wisconsin 53702

Northern Thunder, by

Dick Wachowski, Attorney
310 Water Street
Eau Claire, Wisconsin 54701

FINDINGS OF FACT

1. On September 28, 1978 the Division of Natural Resources Hearings received a stipulation and consent order executed by representatives of the Town of Seymour, the City of Eau Claire and the State of Wisconsin Department of Natural Resources regarding the action brought by the Town of Seymour in docket no. EX-78-49.
2. Said stipulation provides as follows:
    (a) The parties hereby recognize that the City of Eau Claire is in the process of obtaining licensing from DNR of a sanitary land-fill site ("Seven Mile Creek landfill") located upon the following described property:

    A parcel of land located in the east one-half of the southeast one-quarter of Section 8, Township 27 North, Range 8 West, the southwest quarter of the southeast quarter of Section 8, Township 27 North, Range 8 West, lying east of the Seven Mile Creek, and the northwest quarter of the northeast quarter of Section 17, Township 27 North, Range 8 West, lying east of Seven Mile Creek being approximately 150 acres in size.

    (b) The Town of Seymour has objected to the establishment of said landfill site, and the parties hereto have mediated their differences under the auspices of the Wisconsin Center for Public Policy, Madison, Wisconsin.
    (c) This agreement is entered into as the agreement reached pursuant to said mediations, following formal approval by the Town Board of the Town of Seymour, City Council of the City of Eau Claire, and DNR.
    (d) This stipulation may be used by any party hereto as the basis for a consent decree in DNR administrative proceeding EX-78-49, entitled "In the Matter of the Proposed Solid Waste Disposal Facility by the City of Eau Claire Located in the Town of Seymour, Eau Claire County, Wisconsin;" and, further, as the basis for a declaratory judgment in Eau Claire County Circuit Court Case NO. 78CV394, and as the basis for a stipulated dismissal of Eau Claire County Circuit Court Case Nos. 78CV148 and 78CV397; provided, however, that this

stipulation does not constitute a waiver by DNR of its juris-
dictional objections in Eau Claire County Circuit Court Case
Nos. 78CV148, 78CV394, and 78CV397.

3. The examiner has reviewed the stipulation and consent order and
determines that they constitute an appropriate and reasonable
settlement to the proceeding pending before the Division in docket no.
EX-78-49.

CONCLUSIONS OF LAW

1. The Division of Natural Resources Hearings has authority under
sec. 227.075 and sec. 227.012(2), Stats., to conduct a hearing and
order remedial action upon petition therefore by an interested
party.

2. Informal disposition of any contested case prior to hearing may
be made by stipulation, agreed settlement or consent order. See
sec. 227.07(5), Stats.

3. Pursuant to the foregoing Findings of Fact the Division of Natural
Resources Hearings has authority to issue the consent order
hereinafter set out in full.

CONSENT ORDER

1. When an estimated 578,900 tons of waste material and cover material
have been deposited at the Seven Mile Creek landfill, Eau Claire
will close the landfill as soon as the contour plans for Phase I of
said landfill already tentatively approved on July 31, 1978, by DNR
and as shown in the sanitary landfill construction and operational
report, dated May, 1978, and accompanying plans, all of which are
on file in the Department of Public Works, Eau Claire, have been
complied with, and landfill has been properly abandoned in
accordance with the tentative plan approval and state law. Eau Claire
agrees that it will not apply for a license to construct or operate any
phase of the Seven Mile Creek landfill beyond Phase I.

2. Eau Claire will immediately begin construction of a transfer station for
the immediate disposal and consolidation of refuse for transfer to
the landfill site, located in the pre-January 30, 1977 municipal
limits of the City of Eau Claire, as soon as financing can be secured
and as soon as plans for the transfer station have been submitted
by Eau Claire and approved by DNR. Both Eau Claire and DNR
pledge to work speedily to enable construction to begin as soon
as possible. Eau Claire will, as soon as practicable, provide Seymour
with an estimated schedule for construction of the transfer station,
and it is the party's intent that the station be operated by October 1,
1979. Eau Claire shall take all necessary steps to arrange timely
financing and timely submission of the transfer station plans to DNR
for approval so as to permit transfer station construction to begin and

to proceed and to become complete as soon as possible; Eau Claire
represents that the operational date specified herein is reasonable
and realistic considering all relevent circumstances.

3. Eau Claire and Seymour agree that there will be no access permitted
to the Seven Mile Creek landfill except for governmentally licensed
garbage haulers, and, upon securing a permit from the City of
Eau Claire, other persons, firms or corporations who are haulers
of waste or refuse such as wood waste or construction debris as an
integral part of their trade or business which produces the waste or
refuse, and such other vehicles which Eau Claire and Seymour agree
should be permitted access.

Eau Claire and Seymour agree that the ban on such private
vehicular use of the landfill shall take effect when the transfer station
described in paragraph 3 above becomes operational. Eau Claire
agrees, during the interim period, to discourage use of the landfill
by private vehicles.

Eau Claire agrees that it will provide a DNR-approved dumping
box at an approved location for use by residents of Seymour so that
they do not have to travel to the Eau Claire transfer station. The
specific location and methods and procedures for operation of said
dumping box shall be as agreed to by Eau Claire, Seymour and DNR.

4. The attorneys for Seymour and Eau Claire, with the assistance of
DNR, shall draft companion ordinances applicable in their
respective municipalities which shall be patterned after, encompass
and deal with Seymour's concerns now set forth in Ordinance No. 26,
subject to DNR approval. DNR approval of said companion
ordinances is dependent upon compliance with sec. 144.44, Stats.,
after the parties make every reasonable and practical effort to
accomodate the special circumstances and subject matter of the
various disputes and controversies associated with the proposed Seven
Mile Creek landfill site, the foregoing litigation, and the administrative proceedings. It is the intent of this agreement that these
companion ordinances become effective as soon as practicable.

5. If Eau Claire wishes to use the Seymour landfill for disposal of stumps
or similarly innocuous materials, Eau Claire may do so at no cost,
provided DNR provides Eau Claire with a one-time limited use
permit for that purpose. Eau Claire and Seymour agree that, based on
a formula for estimating tonnage calculated by DNR, Seymour will
be permitted to use the Seven Mile Creek landfill at no cost to
Seymour for the deposit of the tonnage of waste equal to the estimated
tonnage placed by Eau Claire in the Seymour landfill.

6. Each party agrees to take all reasonable and positive steps individually
and collectively toward an Eau Claire County or area wide solid
waste system. Additionally, each party shall attempt to secure the
cooperation of any other neighboring municipality or user of the
Seven Mile Creek landfill toward the goal that an Eau Claire County
or area-wide solid waste system be developed.

7. Eau Claire and Seymour agree that at the conclusion of Phase I, as defined in Finding of Fact 2(d) [sic, should be Order Provision No. 1] above, Eau Claire and Seymour will undertake the necessary steps to detach the 150 acres annexed by City of Eau Claire ordinance effective January 30, 1977, for Seven Mile Creek landfill purposes. (Bracketed clause added by the Examiner.)

8. Eau Claire agrees to operate the landfill during hours no longer than 8:00 a.m. to 5:00 p.m., Monday through Friday (8:00 a.m. to 6:00 p.m. during central daylight saving time), and on Saturdays, 8:00 a.m. to 1:00 p.m.

   Eau Claire agrees to minimize the night hours for construction of the landfill and hauling of clay in connection with such construction, and will perform construction and hauling inside the hours of 6:00 a.m. and 10:00 p.m.

9. Each party agrees to the creation of an advisory committee having one member representing each party, which committee will monitor the administration of this stipulation on a continuing basis and which committee shall select a mutually accepted impartial chairperson, and which committee may call on the Wisconsin Center for Public Policy for technical assistance in mediating items of dispute or controversy so as to minimize the liklihood of further litigation or administrative proceedings.

10. All parties agree that this stipulation is subject to modification upon the mutual written consent of all three parties. Any such modification shall be made a part of the consent decree and judgment or orders arising from this stipulation.

11. Seymour agrees to, and hereby does, withdraw all petitions, motions, applications, complaints and similar pleadings and documents filed in DNR administrative proceedings EX-78-49, Eau Claire County Circuit Court Case Nos. 78CV148, 78CV397 and 78CV394; Seymour further agrees to institute no challenges to Eau Claire's pending application for a landfill license, and Seymour agrees to withdraw its appeal from the judgment entered by the Eau Claire County Circuit Court Case No. 77CV109 relating to the annexation of 150 acres from the Town of Seymour herein above described; provided, however, Seymour reserves the right to participate in or challenge any future license applications or renewal thereof with respect to Eau Claire's proposed landfill facility, all as provided by law.

Dated in Madison, Wisconsin: October 10, 1978

STATE OF WISCONSIN DIVISION OF NATURAL RESOURCES HEARINGS

By David H. Schwarz _____

        (signature)

Hearing Examiner

Abbreviations

AAA	American Arbitration Association
ACC	Anaconda Copper Company
APA	Administrative Procedure Act
B/C	benefit/cost analysis
BGD	Boulder-Grand Divide Planning Unit
BWCA	Boundary Waters Canoe Area (Minnesota)
CAA	Clean Air Act Amendments
CCIC	Community Crisis Intervention Center, Washington University, St. Louis, Mo.
CEQ	Council on Environmental Quality
EBA	Environmental Balance Association of Minnesota
EIS	environmental impact statement
ELF	extremely low frequency
ELO	Environmental Liaison Office
EMP	Environmental Mediation Project
EPA	U.S. Environmental Protection Agency
FDA	U.S. Food and Drug Administration
FMCS	Federal Mediation and Conciliation Service
FWPCA	Federal Water Pollution Control Act Amendments
GE	General Electric Company
MERES	Matrix of Environmental Residuals from Energy Systems
MPIRG	Minnesota Public Interest Research Group

NOTES

Adams, Craig. 1975. Telephone interviews. April-July. Mr. Adams works at the Wisconsin State Planning Office, Madison, Wis.

Administrative Procedure Act. 5 U.S.C.A. 706. Scope of review.

Alinsky, Saul D. 1969. *Reveille for Radicals.* N.Y.: Random House. Originally published 1946.

_____. 1971. *Rules for Radicals.* N.Y.: Random House.

Anonymous. 1976. "Science Court: Idea in Search of a Need." *Environmental Science and Technology.* November: 1088-1089.

Baltimore and Potomac Railroad Company v. Fifth Baptist Church. 1883. 103 U.S. 317.

Beane, Marjorie, and John Ross. 1974. "The Role of Technical Information in Decisions on Nuclear Power Plants." Institute for Environmental Studies Report 19, University of Wisconsin, Madison, Wis. September, 154 pp.

The Bible. English King James Version (1962). Reference edition with concordance.

Bilder, Richard B. 1973. "The Role of Unilateral State Action in Preventing International Environmental Injury." University of Wisconsin Sea Grant Report WIS-SG-73-219, Madison, Wis., September.

_____. 1976. "The Settlement of International Environmental Disputes." University of Wisconsin Sea Grant Technical Report 231, Madison, Wis., February, 92 pp.

Boulding, Kenneth. 1962. *Conflict and Defense.* N.Y.: Harper and Row.

Brown, B. 1968. "The Effects of Need to Maintain Face in Interpersonal Bargaining." *Journal of Experimental Social Psychology.* 4:107-122.

_____ . 1970. "Face-saving Following Experimentally Induced Embarrassment." *Journal of Experimental Social Psychology.* 6:255-271.

Brown, R. 1974. "Further Comments on the Risk Shift." *American Psychologist.* 29:468-470.

Browning, Clyde E. 1974. "The Question, "But Is It Geography?" —Revisited or Are There Criteria for Establishing the Geographic Content of Topics?" *Professional Geographer.* 26(2):137-139.

Budowski, G. 1973. "The Current State of World Conservation." *Nature and Resources UNESCO.* January-March, 9(1):19-23.

Burggraf, Frank B., Jr. 1975. Comments on the letter of Scott Mernitz to Commissioner Edward Berlin, N.Y. Public Service Commission (draft). 28 November, 2 pp.

Busterud, John, Vaughn, Barbara. 1979. "The New Trend: Mediation, Not Litigation." *Solid Wastes.* February.

Caldwell, Lynton K. 1971. *Environment: A Challenge to Modern Society.* N.Y.: Doubleday.

California Law Revision Commission. 1970. "Arbitration in Condemnation Cases; A Recommendation of the California Law Revision Commission." *Urban Lawyer.* 2:532-541.

Carpenter, Susan L., and W.J.D. Kennedy. 1977. "Information Sharing and Conciliation: Tools for Environmental Conflict Management." *Environmental Comment* (Urban Land Institute). May, 21-22.

Carter, Luther J. 1979. "Public Support for Environmental Protection Remains Strong."*Science.* 203(4376): 154.

Clark, Peter. 1978. Final report on phase one of developing methods for environmental-energy dispute settlement. Submitted by Research Instit. Am. Arbit. Assoc., to the Council on Environmental Quality and Resource and Land Investigation (RALI) Program, U.S. Geological Survey. Prepared by Clark-McGlennon Assocs. June.

Clean Air Act Amendments. 1970. 42 U.S.C. 1857, *et seq.*

Coastal Zone Management Act. 1972. 86 Stat. 1280, *et seq.*

Coastal Zone Management Newsletter. 1975. 5 February, 6(6):1.

Coberly-Manson, C. 1973. The Chippewa Flowage controversy. University-Industry Research Program, University of Wisconsin, Madison, Wis., 36 pp.

Cohen, Alana. 1972. *Community Crisis Intervention Project,* 10/1/70-9/30/72. Social Science Institute, Washington University, St. Louis, Mo., 55 pp.

Coleman, James S. 1957. *Community Conflict* (monograph). N.Y.: Free Press.

Colorado Land Use Commission. 1977. Agreement and consent to withdrawal of Land Use Commission actions (Thompson and Valentine Highland Park Addition, Durango, Colorado). 24 May, 5 pp.

Community Crisis Intervention Center. 1972. Case study outline (mimeo). Washington University, St. Louis, Mo.

Community Crisis Intervention Project. 1972. Preparing for negotiations (pamphlet). Social Science Institute, Washington University, St. Louis, Mo., 18 pp.

Conservation Foundation Newsletter. 1969. Environmental law issue. 30 September.

Cormick, Gerald W. 1973. "Environmental Mediation: An Action Proposal." Community Crisis Intervention Center, Washington University, St. Louis, Mo., 29 November, 18 pp.

_____ . 1974. "Resolving Environmental Disputes Through Mediation: A Workshop." Paper presented at Environment '74 International Symposium III, Spokane, Wash., 28-30 October, 15 pp.

_____ . 1976. "Mediating Environmental Controversies: Perspectives and First Experience." Prepared for submission to *The Earth Law Journal.* April, 17 pp.

_____ .1977a. Correspondence with author. 13 January. Mr. Cormick is director of the Office of Environmental Mediation, University of Washington, Seattle.

—————— . 1977b. Telephone interview. 1 March.

Cormick, Gerald W., and Jane McCarthy. 1974. "Environmental Mediation: A First Dispute." Community Crisis Intervention Center, Environmental Mediation Project, Washington University, St. Louis, Mo., 20 December, 6 pp.

Cormick, Gerald W., and Leah K. Patton. 1977a. "Environmental Mediation: Defining the Process Through Experience." Office of Environmental Mediation, Institute for Environmental Studies, University of Washington, Seattle, February, 28 pp. (Paper prepared for American Association for the Advancement of Science Symposium on Environmental Mediation Cases, Denver, Colorado.)

Cormick, Gerald W., and Leah K. Patton. 1977b. "Environmental Mediation: Potentials and Limitations." *Environmental Comment.* (Urban Land Institute) May: 13-16.

Coser, Lewis A. 1956. *The Functions of Social Conflict.* Glencoe, Ill.: Free Press.

—————— . 1967. *Continuities in the Study of Social Conflict.* N.Y.: Free Press.

Cota, Sandra. 1975. "Project Seafarer Stirs a Storm in Peninsula." *Milwaukee Journal.* 14 December.

Coulson, Robert. 1973. *How to Stay Out of Court.* N.Y.: Award Books.

Council of State Governments. 1974. "A Legislator's Guide to Land Management." Lexington, Ky.

Council on Environmental Quality. 1973. *Environmental Quality.* Fourth annual report. Washington, D.C.: U.S. Govt. Printing Office, 499 pp.

Council on Environmental Quality. 1976. *Environmental Quality.* Seventh annual report. Washington, D.C.: U.S. Govt. Printing Office, 378 pp.

Council on Environmental Quality. 1978. NEPA implementation of procedural versions; final regulations. 43 Fed. Reg. 55997, et seq. 29 November.

Crisis and Change (newsletter). 1972. Community Crisis Intervention Center, Washington University, St. Louis, Mo., 2(1):1-2.

Current Developments. Vol 10, No. 8. cited on page 76.

Dahl, R.A., and Lindblom, C.E. 1953. *Politics, Economics, and Welfare.* N.Y.: Harper and Row.

Dahrendorf, Ralf. 1959. *Class and Class Conflict in Industrial Society.* Stanford, Calif.: Stanford University Press.

Davis, Allen. 1979. Project Manager, Hudson River PCB Reclamation Project, New York Department of Environmental Conservation, Albany, N.Y. Telephone Interview. 29 May.

Dayton, Charles K. 1976. Letter to Catherine Helgeland. 28 April. Ms. Helgeland is a M.S. candidate, Department of Geography, University of Wisconsin, Madison. Mr. Dayton is an attorney representing MPIRG and the Sierra Club in the BWCA litigation.

Deutsch, Morton. 1973. *The Resolution of Conflict.* New Haven, Conn.: Yale University Press.

DiMento, Joseph F. 1975. "The Citizen Suit: An Added Tool for Environmental Management." *Great Lakes Basin Communicator.* January: 3-5.

Dorfman, R., and H.D. Jacoby. 1971. A model of public decisions illustrated by a water pollution policy problem. In L.L. Roos, ed., *The Politics of Eco-Suicide.* N.Y.: Holt, Rinehart and Winston, pp. 152-219.

Doud, Alden L. 1972. "International Environmental Developments: Perceptions of Developing and Developed Countries." *Natural Resources Journal.* 12:(4):520-529.

Downs, Anthony. 1973. "The Political Economy of Improving Our Environment." In J.S. Bain, ed., *Environmental Decay— Economic Causes and Remedies.* Boston: Little, Brown and Co., pp. 59-81.

Ela, Jonathan. 1974. Telephone interview, 18 April. Mr. Ela is Midwest Representative for the Sierra Club in Madison, Wisconsin.

Environment Action Bulletin. 1975. New unit to referee environmental disputes. 18 October:7.

Environmental Consensus. Vol. 2, No. 1, Vol. 2, No. 2. cited on page 76.

Environmental Law Reporter: 1972. NEPA - reform in government decisionmaking. 2 ELR 50025, *et seq.* (Reprinted from CEQ third annual report, 1972, Chapter 7.)

Environmental Law Reporter. 1973. Litigation under the Clean Air Act. 3 ELR 10007, *et seq.*

Fall, J.C. 1972. "A Study of the Role of Arbitration in the Judicial Process." California Judicial Council, 119 pp.

Federal Water Pollution Control Act Amendments. 1972. 33 U.S.C. 1251, *et seq.*

Feldman, Paul. 1976. "Teachers Pass Credit Around." *Wisconsin State Journal (Madison).* 19 January.

Fisher, Gary. 1976. "A Citizens' View of Land Use in Colorado. "Colorado Land Use Commission, Denver, Colo., December, 84 pp.

Fogarty, John. 1978. "How Tahoe Pact Was Ironed Out." *San Francisco Chronicle.* 19 September.

Foster, Charles H.W. 1969. "A Case for Environmental Conciliation." Paper presented at the Annual Meeting of the American Institute of Biological Sciences, University of Vermont, Burlington, Vt., 19 August, 5 pp.

_____ . 1975a. Personal correspondence with author. 14 April. Charles Foster has worked for Arthur D. Little, Inc., Cambridge, Mass., and was formerly Secretary of the Massachusetts Executive Office of Environmental Affairs.

_____ . 1975b. Personal correspondence with author. 26 August.

Fradin, David. 1976. Telephone interview with author. 18 May. Mr. Fradin is Executive Vice President of Environmental Balance Association of Minnesota, Inc., St. Paul, the organization which successfully mediated the Moorhead, Minn. dispute.

Fradin, David. 1977. Personal correspondence with author. 19 January.

Freeman, David M. 1976. "A Social Well-being Analysis of the Impacts of Four Management Alternatives for the Boulder-Grand Divide Planning Unit." Colorado State University, Ft. Collins, 4 May.

Gabor, Dennis. 1970. *Innovations: Scientific, Technological, and Social.* N.Y.: Oxford University Press.

Galanter, Marc. 1973. "Why the "Haves" Come Out Ahead: Speculations on the Limits of Legal Change." Unpub. manuscript, fifth draft. August. SUNY-Buffalo, N.Y.

Gilbert, Bil. 1976. "My Country 'Tis of Thee." *Sports Illustrated.* 20-27 December.

Glacken, Clarence J. 1956. "Changing Ideas In the Habitable World." In William L. Thomas, Jr., ed., *Man's Role in Changing the Face of the Earth,* Vol. 1. Chicago: Univ. of Chicago Press, pp. 70-92.

Hall, Jon. 1973. Conflict Management Survey (booklet and interpretation manual). Conroe, Texas: Teleometrics International.

Handlin, Oscar. 1959. *Boston's Immigrants.* Cambridge, Mass.: Harvard University Press.

Hanly v. Kliendienst. 1972. 471 F. 2d. 823. U.S. Court of Appeals, Second Circuit. 5 December.

Hardin, Garrett, 1968. "The Tragedy of the Commons." *Science.* 162:1243-1248.

Hart, Henry C. 1974. "Toward a Political Science of Water Resources Decisions." In L. Douglas James, ed., *Man and Water.* Louisville, Ky.: University Press, pp. 122-163.

Haveman, Robert. 1975. Guest lecture, Environmental Economics 343 (Prof Cichetti). University of Wisconsin, Madison, 15 April.

Heberlein, Thomas A. 1974. "The Three Fixes: Technological, Cognitive, and Structural." In Donald R. Field, *et al,* eds., *Water and Community Development.* Ann Arbor, Mich.: Ann Arbor Science Pubs., Inc.

Helgeland, Catherine. 1976. Wilderness philosophy and environmental research in land use disputes. Boundary Waters Canoe Area. Rough draft, M.S. thesis, Dept. of Geography, University of Wisconsin, Madison.

Hermann, M.G., and N. Kogan. 1968. "Negotiations in Leader and Delegate Groups." *Journal of Conflict Resolution.* 12(3): 332-344.

Hill, Gladwin, 1976. "Huge Power Plant Dropped after Long Fight in Utah." *N.Y. Times.* 15 April.

Holmes, J.G., W.F. Throop, and L.H. Strickland. 1971. "Effects of Pre-negotiation Expectations on the Distributive Bargaining Process." *Journal of Experimental Social Psychology.* 7: 582-599.

Hoshko, John. 1979. Commander, U.S. Navy Public Affairs Office, Office of ELF Program Coordination, Dept. of Defense, Washington, D.C. Telephone interview. 29 May.

Hudson, Barclay M., Martin Wachs, and Joseph L. Schofer. 1974. "Local Impact Evaluation in the Design of Large Scale Urban Systems." *Jour. Am. Instit. of Planners.* 40(4):255-265.

Huntington, Ellsworth. 1924. *Civilization and Climate.* New Haven, Conn.: Yale University Press.

Ingram, Helen M. 1969. *Patterns of Politics in Water Resources Development: A Case Study of New Mexico's Role in the Colorado River Basin Bill.* Albuquerque: University of New Mexico Press.

Jaffe, Louis L., and Laurence H. Tribe. 1971. *Environmental Protection.* Chicago: Bracton Press.

Karaganis, Joseph. 1976. Telephone interview. 25 May. Mr. Karaganis is an attorney representing railroad and environmental interests in the Lock and Dam 26 litigation.

Karan, Pradyumna P. 1971. "Diving the Water: A Problem in Political Geography." *Professional Geographer.* 13(1):6-10.

Karlstrand, Einar W. 1976. "Environmental Mediation: A New Tool." *Duluth (Minn.) News-Tribune.* 18 January.

Kaye, Phyllis E. 1971. "Resolving Conflict Through Mediation." In J. Kerry Smith, ed., *Issues in Higher Education 1971.* Jossay-Bass, pp. 163-171.

Knelman, Fred H. 1971. *1984 and All That.* Belmont, Calif.: Wadsworth Pub. Co., Inc.

Koch, Howard E., Jr., *et al.* 1960. "Geography and International Conflict." *Journal of Conflict Resolution.* 4(1):1-13.

Kogan, N., H. Lamm, and G. Trommsdorff. 1972. "Negotiation Constraints in the Risk-taking Domain: Effects of Being Observed by Partners of Higher or Lower Status." *Journal of Personality and Social Psychology.* 23(2):143-156.

Kurtz-Phelan, James. 1977. Telephone interview. 1 September. Mr. Kurtz Phelan is Assistant Attorney General for the State of Colorado, representing the Colorado Land Use Commission and Colorado Highway Department.

Lake, Laura. 1977. "Mediating Electric Power Plant Options for California: A Case Study of Conflict Avoidance" (draft). Department of Environmental Science and Engineering, University of California, Los Angeles, February, 23 pp.

Landau, Norman J., and Paul D. Rheingold. 1971. *The Environmental Law Handbook.* N.Y.: Ballantine.

Laughlin, William S. 1975. "Aleuts: Ecosystem, Holocene History, and Siberian Origin." *Science.* 189:507-515.

Leighty, Leighton L. 1971. "Aesthetics as a Legal Basis for Environmental Control." 17 *Wayne Law Review* 1347. (Nov.-Dec., No. 5).

Lorenson, Burman. 1977. Letter to Mr. L.A. Amicarella, U.S.F.S., Ft. Collins, Colo. 2 February. Mr. Lorenson is Socio-Economic Impact Coordinator for the State of Colorado.

Lord, William B., and Maurice L. Warner. 1973. "Aggregates and Externalities: Information Needs for Public Natural Resource Decision-making." *Natural Resources Journal.* 13(1): 106-117.

Lowi, Theodore J. 1964. "American Business, Public Policy, Case Studies and Political Theory." Reprinted in Randall B. Ripley, ed., *Public Policies and Their Politics.* N.Y.:W.W. Norton (1966).

Manko, Joseph. 1976. Telephone interview. 28 October. Mr. Manko is former regional counsel for the EPA.

Marsh, George P. 1864. *Man and Nature.* N.Y.: Scribner's Ed. by David Lowenthal.

McCarthy, Jane. 1974. "Environmental Disputes: A New Challenge for the Negotiation-mediation Process." *Conflict* (newsletter), Institute for Mediation and Conflict Resolution, N.Y., 2(1):3.

——————. 1977. Telephone interview. 15 February. Ms. McCarthy worked previously with Cormick (see reference) in one of the first formal environmental mediation efforts.

McCloskey, Michael. 1977. "On Loggerheadedness." *N.Y. Times.* 20 September. Mr. McCloskey is executive director of the Sierra Club.

Mernitz, Scott. 1975. "Geography and Mediation of Environmental Disputes." In "Communications from Readers," *Professional Geographer.* 27(4):491-492.

——————. 1976. "Mediation of Environmental Disputes Could Save Time, Money, Resources." "In My Opinion" Column, *Milwaukee Journal.* 19 February.

Mikesell, Marvin. 1960. "Comparative Studies in Frontier History." *Annals of the Association of American Geographers.* (March): 62-74.

Milwaukee Journal. 1975. "Chippewa Falls Gets Its Back Up Over Odors." 14 October.

Mishan, E.J. 1973. *Economics for Social Decisions.* N.Y.: Praeger.

Moya, Frank. 1977. "Pat Schroeder Asks Foothills Be Mediated." *Rocky Mountain News (Denver).* 17 July.

Mumford, Lewis. 1970. *The Pentagon of Power,* N.Y.: Harcourt Brace Jovanovich.

Murphy, Evelyn F. 1976. Personal correspondence with author. 26 January. Evelyn Murphy is currently Secretary of the Massachusetts Executive Office of Environmental Affairs.

Murphy, Michael. 1971. "Comment: A Case for Air Pollution as a Mandatory Bargaining Subject." 51 *Oregon Law Review* 223.

Myers, D.G., and H. Lamm. 1975. "The Polarizing Effect of Group Discussion." *American Scientist.* 63:297-303.

National Environmental Policy Act. 1970. 42 U.S.C. 4321, *et seq.*

National Transportation Safety Board. 42 U.S.C.A. 1902. Selection and appointment of officers and employees.

National Wildlife. 1976. Environmental quality index. 3 February: 17-29.

Nelson, David R. 1976. "Phosphate Lode Boomerangs for Town." *Milwaukee Journal.* 8 February.

Nelson, Gaylord. 1970. "Five Who Care." *Look.* 21 April: 33.

Nicolau, George, and Gerald W. Cormick. 1972. "Community Disputes and the Resolution of Conflict: Another View." *Arbitration Journal.* 27(2):98-112.

Noise Control Act. 1972. 42 U.S.C. 4901, *et seq.*

Nye, Donna. 1977. Telephone interview. 17 October. Ms. Nye works in the Boulder, Colorado, office of the National Audobon Society.

Ogburn, William F. 1957. "The Meaning of Technology." Reprinted in Fred H. Knelman, ed., *1984 and All That* (1971). Belmont, Calif.: Wadsworth, pp. 4-9.

Pinchot, Gifford. 1910. *The Fight for Conservation.* Seattle: University of Washington Press (reprinted 1967).

Playboy. 1976. "What's Really Happening on Campus." October: 169.

Podell, J.E., and W.M. Knapp. 1969. "The Effect of Mediation on Perceived Firmness of the Opponent." *Journal of Conflict Resolution.* 13(4):511-520.

Pruitt, D.G., and J.L. Andrews. 1969. "Effect of Time Pressure, Time Elapsed and Opponent's Concession Rate on Behavior in Negotiation." *Journal of Experimental Social Psychology.* 5:43-60.

Reitze, Arnold W., Jr., and Glenn I. Reitze. 1974. "The Costs of Litigation." *Environment.* 16(6):3-4

Reserve Mining v. U.S. 1974. 6 ERC 1618.

RESOLVE. 1978. *Environmental Mediation—An Effective Alternative?* A report on a conference held in Reston, Va., 11-13 January. Co-sponsored by Aspen Institute for Humanistic Studies and Sierra Club Foundation.

RESOLVE. 1979. RARE II methodology report. Palo Alto, Calif.

Resources. 1971. Resources for the Future, Inc., newsletter. (January) 36:8-9.

Ridgeway, J. 1970. *The Politics of Ecology.* N.Y.: Dutton.

Rivkin, Malcolm D. 1977. "Negotiated Development: A Breakthrough in Environmental Controversies." *Environmental Comment* (Urban Land Instit.) May: 3-6.

Ruff, Larry E. 1973. "The Economic Common Sense of Pollution." In Alan C. Enthoven and A. Myrick Freeman III, eds., *Pollution, Resources, and the Environment.* N.Y.: W.W. Norton, pp. 37-53.

Sagar, Lawrence G. 1976. "Keeping the Cities Down to Size." N.Y. Times. 29 August.

Science. 1976. Experiment planned to test feasibilitly of a 'science court.' 193:129.

Seattle Times. 1974. " 'Miracle' Agreement on Snoqualmie." 22 December.

Semple, Ellen C. 1901. The Anglo-Saxons of the Kentucky Mountains. Reprinted in R.S. Platt, ed., *Field Studies in American Geography* (1959). Chicago: University of Chicago Press, pp. 60-77.

Severo, Richard. 1976. "2 Million Offer by GE Reported in Pollution Case." *N.Y. Times.* 25 April.

Sierra Club v. Froehlke. 1973. 359 F. Supp. 1289. U.S. District Court, S.D. Texas, Houston Division. 16 February.

Sierra Club v. Morton. 1972. 2 ELR 20192. U.S. Supreme Court, No. 70-34. 19 April.

Simkin, William E. 1971. *Mediation and the Dynamics of Collective Bargaining.* Washington, D.C.: Bureau of National Affairs.

Simmel, Georg. 1955. *Conflict.* Trans. by Kurt H. Wolff. Glencoe, Ill.: Free Press.

Spindler, George, and Louise Spindler. 1971. *Dreamers Without Power: The Menomini Indians.* N.Y.: Holt, Rinehart, and Winston.

State of Colorado. 1974. Colorado House Bill No. 1041: An act concerning land use, and providing for identification, designation, and administration of areas and activities of state interest, and assigning additional duties to the Colorado Land Use Commission and the Department of Local Affairs, and making appropriations thereof.

Stratton, Owen, and Philip Sirotkin. 1959. *The Echo Park Controvery.* Inter-University Case Program, Inc. #46. Indianapolis, Ind.: Bobbs-Merrill, 100 pp.

Straus, Donald B. 1973. An application to the Rockefeller Foundation for a fellowship in conflict in international relations. American Arbitration Association, N.Y., 1 December, 13 pp.

——————. 1977. "Mediating Environmental, Energy, and Economic Trade-offs." Research Institute, American Arbitration Association, N.Y., February, 38 pp. + appendices.

Taylor, Warren L. 1970. "The Expectations and Values of the Mediator." Comments delivered at a briefing conference sponsored by the Federal Bar Association and the Bureau of National Affairs, 12-13 October, 12 pp.

Turner, Frederick J. 1893. "The Significance of the Frontier in American History." *Annual Report of the American Historical Association* (Washington, D.C., 1894. Reprinted in Frederick J. Turner, *The Frontier in History* (1920). N.Y.: Henry Holt.

U.S. Forest Service. 1976. Draft environmental statement for the Boulder-Grand Divide Unit (Colorado). U.S.D.A. Forest Service, Rocky Mt. Region. 8 November, 208 pp.

U.S. Forest Service. 1977. Piedra land management planning and wild and scenic rivers study (information paper). U.S.D.A. Forest Service, Rocky Mt. Region. 3 January.

U.S. v. Reserve Mining. 1974a. 6 ERC 1449. U.S. District Court (Minnesota), No. 5-72 Civil 19. 20 April. Essential Findings of fact and conclusions of law.

U.S. v. Reserve Mining. 1974b. 6 ERC 1657. U.S. District Court (Minnesota), No. 5-72 Civil 19. 11 May. Supplementary findings of fact, conclusions of law and memorandum.

U.S. Water Resources Council. 1976. "Principles and Standards for Planning." Fed. Reg., Vol. 38, No. 174, (Part III).

Wagar, J.A. 1970. "The Challenge of Environmental Education." *Today's Education."* 59(9):14-18.

Ways, Max. 1970. "How to Think About the Environment." *Fortune.* (February).

Wehr, Paul. 1976. "Environmental Peacemaking" (preliminary report). Institute of Behavioral Science, University of Colorado, Boulder, Colo. 15 June, 62 pp.

White, Gilbert F. 1969. *Strategies of American Water Management.* Ann Arbor: University of Michigan Press.

White, Lynn, Jr. 1967. "The Historic Roots of Our Ecologic Crisis." *Science.* 155:1203-1207.

Wilderness Society v. Morton. 1973. 2 ELR 20085.

Wisconsin Environmental Policy Act. Wisconsin Statutes, Sec. 1.11, et seq.

Wisconsin Shoreland Zoning Act. Wisconsin Statutes, Secs. 59.971 and 144.26.

Wood, Colin J.B. 1976. "Conflict in Resource Management and the Use of Threat: The Goldstream Controversy." *Natural Resources Journal.* 16(1):137-158.

Zile, Zigurds L. 1974. "A Legislative-political History of the Coastal Zone Management Act of 1972." *Coastal Zone Management Journal.* 1(3):235-274.

Index

Assimilative capacity, of the environment, 127
Associated Industries, New York, 87
Attorney general, Wisconsin, 37
Attributes, of mediable disputes, 121
Audubon Society, 6
Aurora, North Carolina, 115, 118
Authoritarian nature, of ethnic groups, 57
Authority, of an agency, 139
Automobile, 3, 29

B

Balance of power, and conflict, 51ff
Balancing of interests, 3, 8, 9, 14, 28, 31ff, 66
Baldus, Rep. Alvin (Wisconsin), 95
Baltimore and Potomac Railroad Company v. Fifth Baptist Church, 46
Bargaining, 158ff
 —atmosphere for, 157
Barge operators, 124
Barge traffic, on rivers, 98
Barley malting plant, 116
Beane, Marjorie, 17
Beaufort County, North Carolina, 115
Bedrock, conductivity of, 102
Behavior
 —human, 19
 —of groups in conflict, 50, 159
 —of individuals in conflict, 54, 159
 —during negotiations, 160
Benefit/cost analysis, 27, 31, 101, 111, 123
Benefit/cost ratio, 61
Benefits, public, 142
"Best practicable" water treatment, 28
"Big picture," 148
Bilateral task force negotiations, 75
Bilder, Richard B., 58, 79, 81, 117
Biological waste conversion, 21
Biology, 73
Biomass, 15
Blue-collar workers, 142
Blue Line, for utilities, 147
"Bottom Line," 53
Boulder-Grand Divide Planning Unit (BGD) USFS (Colorado), 26
Boulding, Kenneth. 53, 57
Boundaries, of disputes, 143
Boundary Waters Canoe Area (BWCA), Minnesota, 104, 120, 127, 130
Bright, Judge (U. S. Court of Appeals, St. Louis), 66
British Columbia, 70, 137

Brown, B., 56
Brown, R., 54
Browning, Clyde E., 146
Budowski, G., 15
Bureau of Reclamation, U. S., 154
Burggraf, Frank B. Jr., 146
Burley, New York Conservation Commissioner, 88
Burning, controlled, of forests, 104
Business, 2, 14
 —enterprise, 6
Busterud, John, 37, 72
Butte, Montana, 114

C

Caldwell, Lynton, 7
California, 73, 110, 127
California Law Revision Commission, 44
California, University of, Los Angeles, 71
Camping, primitive, 104
Canada, 84
Cancer, 84, 86, 107, 114
Canoeing, 104
Carey, Governor Hugh (New York), 87, 140
Carpenter, Susan, 71, 74
Carter, Luther, 20
Case law, 23ff, 28, 31, 34
 —environmental, 130
Case studies
 —of environmental conflict, 79
 —mediation, 25
Catalyst, 42
 —third party as, 133
Categories, 79
Caucuses, 48, 158
 —private, during negotiations, 53
Center for Energy Policy, Boston, 71
Center for Public Policy, Madison, 119
Chamber of Commerce, 115
Change, and compromise, 59
Check lists, 148
Chicago, 112
Chippewa Falls, Wisconsin, 115, 119
Chronological nature of disputes, 81
Chronology, of a dispute (conflict), 54, 89, 133
Citizen action groups, 130
Citizen (civil) suit provisions, 29ff, 47
Citizen participation process, 148
Civil rights, 21
Civilization and Climate
 (Huntington), 4

Injury, public, 142
Institute of Mediation and Conflict
    Resolution, New York City, 43
Institutional responsibilities and
    constraints on negotiations, 159
Institutions, 15
    —for mediation services, 72
Integrator, mediator as, 58, 65
Intelligentsia, Western, 57
Intensity of dispute, 156
Interalternative analysis, 26
Interdisciplinary analysis, 17
    —of environmental conflict, 150
Interdisciplinary nature, of environ-
    mental conflict, 160
Interest groups, 148
Interests, diffuse, and dispute
    resolution, 74
Interior, U. S. Dept. of, 69
International
    —conflict, 149
    —dispute settlement, 73
    —environmental disputes, 79
Interstate 90 dispute, Seattle, 70ff, 78
Intervenors, 10, 42, 84, 96, 141
    —defined as used in this text, 40
    —indirect and covert, 161
    —legal, 130, 143
Intervention, 48, 52, 58
    —active, 40
    —defined as used in this text, 40
    —legal, 40
    —passive, 40
Interviews, 133
Irrigation, 16
Isolation, geographic, and environ-
    mental conflict, 154
Issues, 25, 31, 118, 148, 156
    —litigable v. real-life, 130
Izaak Walton League, 6

J

Jackson, Senator Henry, 14
Jacoby, H. D., 11, 27
Jaffe, Louis L., 31
Jim Bridger Power Plant, Wyoming,
    113
Jobs versus environment conflict, 46
Judge, 77
    —posture of trial judge, 130
Jurisdiction, political, 146
Justice Department, Wisconsin, 37, 85

K

Kaiparowits power plant, Utah, 102,
    120, 127, 162
Karaganis, Joseph, 124
Karlstrand, Einar W., 70
Kaye, Phyllis E., 43
Kennecott Copper Corp., 116
Kennedy, W. J. D., 74
Kerosene, 111
Kickapoo Dam, Wisconsin, 140
Kickapoo River, Wisconsin, 69, 94,
    120
Kissinger, Henry, 73
Knapp, W. M., 55
Knelman, Fred, 3
Koch, Howard E. Jr., 149
Kogan, N., 55ff
Kurtz-Phelan, James, 139

L

Labor disputes, 39
    —mediation in, 43
    —mediators of, 67
    —settlement, 73
Labor-management
    —disputes, 149
    —negotiations, 58
    —relations, 43, 55, 127
Labor relations, 40, 49, 53
Labor unions, 44
Ladysmith, Wisconsin, 116
Laissez-faire technology, 4
Lake currents, 147
Lake, Laura, 71
Lake Powell, 110
Lake Superior, 82, 100
Lamm, H., 55ff
Land resources disputes, 82, 100
Land use, 10, 16ff, 29ff, 78, 115, 146,
    156
    —conflicts, 115
    —planning, 92
Landau, Norman J., 86
Landfill, sanitary, 37
Laughlin, William, 6
Law, 73
    —environmental, 8, 21, 28, 47
    —federal environmental, 32
Laws
    —federal, 18, 24, 32, 46
    —state, 18, 24, 28

Positive attributes of conflict, 62
Power plants, 4
—coal fired, 15ff, 110ff
—nuclear, 17, 60, 110
"Prejudice," dismissal with, 77
Pre-negotiations efforts, 156, 159
"Pre-negotiations stage" of conflict, 133
Preservation, 6, 16, 111, 127ff
—interests, 126, 140
—of agricultural land, 16, 115
—of natural areas, 94
—wilderness, 30
President, Executive Office of the, 99, 103, 108, 118
Prima facie case, 86
Priorities, ranking of, for parties to environmental conflict, 160ff
Problem-solving, 42
Procedures
—legal, 48
—mediation, 123
Products, commercial, 29
Professional Geographer, 68
Profits, 6, 14, 85
Property rights, 11, 161
Proponent, development, 126
Proposition 13 (California), 20
Proxmire, Senator William (Wisconsin), 94, 102
Pruitt, D. G., 56
Psychological aspects, of mediation, 50
Psychological needs, of negotiating parties, 133
Psychology, 39, 73, 120, 150
—literature of, and the conflict situation, 50
—of negotiating groups, 160
Public good, 46, 61, 141
Public hearings, parties to, 132
Public interest, 34
—group representatives, 33
—research groups, 130
Public Interest Research Group, Minnesota, 106
Public Intervenor, Wisconsin, 37
Public lands, 28
Public opinion, 124, 141
Public participation, 27
Public policy decision, 99
"Public rights," 37
Public service projects (by industry), 14
Public support for environmental objectives, 20
Public welfare, 10, 11, 15, 61

Q

Quality of life, 16, 82, 112, 115, 127
Quantification of environmental amenities, 31
Questionnaires, 148

R

Racial discrimination, 119
Radiation, ultraviolet, 107
Radical groups, 44
Radio, 17
Railways, 29, 98, 124, 142
Rampton, Governor Calvin (Utah), 111
RARE II (Roadless Area Review and Evaluation, Phase II), 74
Reasonableness, 157
Record
—of negotiated settlement, 132
—written, of a dispute, 133
Recreation, 17, 69, 92, 94, 104, 131
Recreational areas, national, 110
Recreational lands, management plans for, 24
Redistributive decision, 99, 142
Referee, 66
Referenda, 10, 101, 103
Referral services, for mediators, 72
Regional factors, and environmental conflict, 155
Regulation, 24, 142
—environmental, 113, 116, 126, 128
—of conflict, 59
Regulatory
—arena, 156
—conflicts, 33
—decisions, 98, 142
—process, 47
Reid, Ogden, 87, 140
Reitze, Arnold W. Jr., 48
Reitze, Glenn I., 48
"Repeat players" (RP), 128
Representative group, for negotiations, 54
Representatives, to a negotiating group, 92
Researchers, 14
Reserve Mining Company, Minnesota, 47, 82, 98, 106, 108, 117, 120, 130, 135, 143, 147, 156
Reserve Mining v. U. S., 66
Reservoir development, 131
Residuals, 143

Y

Z